MY DARK
SECRET

MY DARK SECRET

DAWN HEMMINGS

atmosphere press

Published by Atmosphere Press

Cover design by Kevin Stone

Atmospherepress.com

Dedicated to Ryan, who gave me the confidence to actually start writing this book – thank you

CHAPTERS

Preface

Deep within the recesses of every individual's life, concealed beneath layers of smiles and shared stories, lie secrets. These concealed truths vary in magnitude, from the innocent pilfering of sweets in childhood to the profound complexities of adult clandestine affairs. Regardless of their weight, we all bear secrets, and it is this mysterious dimension of human existence that binds us together. Yet, within the mosaic of these concealed realities, there are some secrets that transcend the ordinary, veiled in shadows so profound that even the one who harbours them quakes with fear at the thought of their revelation.

For me, such a secret exists, its darkness casting a long, unsettling shadow over my life. It is a secret so deeply buried that even the faintest glimmer of its existence terrifies me. Throughout my existence, this enigma has remained shrouded in silence, hidden from prying eyes, and shielded from the probing curiosity of others. It is a secret I have carried alone, a menacing presence lurking in the deepest corners of my soul, and a truth I have never dared to share with another soul. So, let me tell you about me and my secret.

Who Am I?

My name is Isla Wild, and to most, I seem like any other woman, cloaked in the routine of her daily life. In the comfortable stillness of my home, I live accompanied solely by my feline friend, Apollo, a giant male Maine Coon, a silent partner in my isolated existence.

By day, I immerse myself in the world of books, working diligently at the local library, surrounded by shelves filled with endless tales and knowledge. I've been employed at the library since my college days, and my love for books has never diminished. It's a place where I can indulge in my reading preferences freely. Being an introvert, I often find solace within the pages of the books I devour. They serve as my refuge, allowing me to escape from the realities of life whenever I need to.

I have been blessed with an innate attractiveness, though I often underestimate its power. Opting for a casual and comfortable style, I find joy in expressing my authentic self through the clothes I wear. Laughter is my language, and I relish the ability to bring smiles to the faces of those around me. There's something magical about the sound of genuine laughter, as it creates an instant connection and brightens even the dullest of moments.

Physically, I might not tower over many, but the real magnetism resides in the quiet strength of my appearance. My hair, midnight black and flowing just past my shoulders, provides a stark contrast to the haunting light of my icy blue eyes. Those eyes, laden with secrets, are windows to an inferno of suppressed passions and dreams.

Though the world gives me energy, my heart finds its truest warmth in the love I share with my cherished family. The bond with my mother and sister is an unbreakable thread that weaves through the fabric of my being. A few years ago, we faced the painful loss of my dad, an experience that brought us much closer together. They are my pillars of support, confidants, and partners in joy and sorrow. Together, we navigate the ebb and flow of life, finding solace in the embrace of our shared love and experiences.

In this seemingly ordinary life, there is an extraordinary essence that yearns to be discovered—a spirit that dances in the laughter, lingers in the depths of my eyes, and connects me to the world. It is within the simple moments, the genuine connections, and the love of family and friends that I find my truest sense of fulfilment and purpose. And so, with a heart filled with gratitude and a soul open to the wonders that lie ahead, I continue to embrace the journey of life as Isla Wild, the extraordinary but very ordinary girl.

But don't let me fool you; beneath this seemingly ordinary tapestry, there lies a twisted thread—a haunting secret. I bear a burden that is shrouded in darkness—a secret so profound, so repulsive, that even the weight of it seals me with guilt. A truth so chilling that its mere acknowledgement fills me with an unspeakable dread. A truth that, were it to be uncovered, would shatter the very essence of Isla Wild and shock people to the bone.

Yet, the nature of this secret is far too grim to be shared, not with friends, family, or even the watchful eyes of my feline friend Apollo, for its revelation would surely lead to a cascade of consequences that I am unwilling to face. This lurking darkness sometimes feels like an unbearable weight, gnawing at my conscience, reminding me of what I might be capable of.

There are times when the weight of this secret threatens to consume me, a constant reminder of the darkness that dwells within. It festers in the deepest recesses of my being, twisting and gnawing at my conscience. The knowledge of what I am about to do, or perhaps what I am capable of, is a haunting presence that lingers relentlessly. In fact, it makes me feel physically sick to the stomach.

The mere thought of exposing this part of me, this side that harbours such darkness, sends shivers down my spine. I cannot bear the thought of the judgement, the scorn, or the isolation that would inevitably follow from everyone I know or who knows me. The thoughts I have shock even me.

Thus, I remain trapped in a web of silence, my secret securely locked away, known only to me and the shadows that reside in the corners of my mind. It is a torment to carry this burden alone, unable to seek solace or redemption through confession. The fear of rejection and the loss of everything I hold dear binds my tongue, forcing me into a solitary existence of secrets and shame.

I maintain a circle of friends, but I deliberately keep most of them at a distance, our encounters sporadic, as they are scattered across the country—connections forged during my journeys in my trusty campervan. This deliberate distance allows me to preserve the cocoon of solitude I've woven around myself, both at home and during my travels in the campervan. It's a protective measure, ensuring that I never inadvertently reveal the shrouded depths of my darkest secret, a choice I've made to navigate life's complexities with greater ease.

As I stand daydreaming and washing the dishes, I observe my cat. He remains blissfully unaware of the turmoil within me, and I can't help but envy his simplicity. At times, I find solace in watching my cat, his uncomplicated existence making me yearn for such simple peace. How I long to confide in my loyal companion, to share this dark secret and be comforted by his unwavering presence. But even this loyal, innocent creature with its innocent eyes must be spared the storm raging within me and must be shielded from the darkness that lurks within my soul. He is a natural predator and would only think it normal to feel this way.

The weight of this secret taints every aspect of my life. It casts a shadow over my interactions, colouring them with a tinge of guilt and mistrust. Every smile, every laugh, feels tainted by the knowledge of what lies hidden beneath the surface. It is a burden that I cannot escape, a constant reminder of the fragility of my own humanity. The one constant thought that is always in my head.

And so, I carry on, wearing a mask of normality, concealing the truth that eats away at me from the inside. The guilt gnaws at my conscience, a relentless reminder of the darkness that resides within every one of us. In the depths of solitude, I grapple with the ramifications of my actions, tormented by the knowledge that I am capable of such deeds.

In the still hours of the night, while I lie in my bed, staring up at the ceiling when the world is lost in dreams, my secret becomes a roaring tempest. It whispers in my ear, urging me to confront the truth, to seek redemption, and find a way to release the shackles that bind me. But the overwhelming fear holds me in its icy grasp, keeping me ensnared in this cycle of deceit and guilt.

My dreams are a relentless source of torment, frequently jolting me awake with agonised screams, my heart pounding in my chest and my body drenched in a cold sweat. In the aftermath, I must fumble for the solace of light, its gentle glow soothing the turbulence within me. Yet, despite the nightly turmoil, I am steadfast in my resolve to document every vivid detail of these haunting dreams. In those moments of turmoil, I believe, may lie the elusive keys that could unlock the answers to the uncertain path I am destined to tread.

Hence, my secret stays imprisoned within me, hidden from the world, a dark spectre unknown even to the one creature that loves me unconditionally, Apollo. I tread a lonely path, filled with regret and longing for absolution. But until the day comes when I can find the courage to face the consequences of my impending actions, my secret will remain mine alone, haunting the corridors of my soul, until now..............

My Dark Secret

I want to commit murder....

There, I've said it: I want to commit murder.

Just saying it out loud brings some relief. Admitting it, even to myself, feels like a chilling confession that sends shivers down my spine. The mere act of vocalising such a dark desire carries a strange weight, and yet, absurdly, a hint of release emerges, a grim acknowledgement that I can no longer deny the lurking shadows within me.

There's a saying that suggests, "The devil lies in the details." It's a phrase that has haunted me since childhood, whispering in my ear during long nights and even longer days. It was a mystery, a beckoning hand, leading me towards the inscrutable realms of the mind. The idea of murder—it's more than just an act; it's an art, a dark and mesmerising dance.

In my formative years, I was a typical child, navigating the classroom as the quiet one, engrossed in the world of books and captivated by the realms of fantasy. My parents held a complex blend of emotions regarding my interests—a mix of pride in my budding intellect and concern due to the unconventional nature of my pursuits. While other children were captivated by dolls and fashion, my fascination lay in the enigmatic terrain of human psychology. It was in my early teens that I discovered my profound interest in books, delving into the mysteries of why individuals commit certain acts, particularly the darkest among them: murder. As I now grapple with the unsettling desire that looms on the horizon, I can't help but trace its origins back to those early years of exploring the shadows concealed within the human psyche.

I often found myself questioning the boundaries of human capacity. How do we, as mere mortals, decide what's right and what's wrong? And when presented with the unspeakable, what drives one's actions? More importantly, what fuels the compulsion to act upon one's darkest desires? Are we born with these feelings, or do they come from the environment we live in, the people we engage with, such as family and close friends, or do we learn them from school and education? Lots of questions I am constantly asking myself, trying to find where these thoughts and feelings come from, but I find no answers.

Initially, my fascination with murder was purely academic, or so it seemed at the outset. My mother, sensing the intensification of my interest, had a conversation with me about it one day. I was sitting on my bed, engrossed in a true crime podcast playing on my laptop. She entered my room one evening, her eyes scanning the crime-themed posters plastering my walls. She seemed concerned, so I set aside my laptop and gave her my full attention.

"Hey, Isla, can I come in?" she asked.

I looked up, surprised by her visit. "Sure, Mom. What's up?"

She settled on the edge of my bed, studying my face as she began, "Isla, I've noticed you've been really into these true crime stories lately. It seems like it's all you're interested in."

I couldn't contain my excitement. "Oh, Mom, you won't believe the details of this case! It's so intense. I love figuring out who's done it before they reveal it."

Her expression grew more concerned. "Sweetie, I get that solving mysteries can be exciting, but these are real-life tragedies, not just stories."

I tried to reassure her. "I know, Mom, but it's like piecing together a puzzle. The psychology behind it is fascinating."

She sighed, clearly worried. "Isla, real crime is different. It's not just a game. There's pain and suffering involved. I don't want you to lose sight of that."

I defended my interest, saying, "I'm not glorifying anything, Mom. It's just a hobby, like reading a thrilling novel."

She continued, "I just want to make sure you understand the gravity of it. It's essential to balance your curiosity with empathy."

I argued, "Mom, I'm not planning to become a detective or kill anyone. It's just interesting to me."

She reached across and gave me a tight hug, still concerned but hoping I'd take her words to heart. "I know you won't, sweetheart. I just want you to keep a balance. Now, how about we find a good movie to watch together?"

However, over time my mom didn't believe me, and she took me to a therapist named Dr. Elaine Morris, an imposing figure with piercing eyes. She was a formidable presence, yet her attempts to probe the depths of my psyche couldn't deter me from my escalating passion. Over time, as Dr. Morris grew to understand me better and recognise that I was not a disturbed child, she offered me a curated list of recommended readings—comprising books on criminal psychology, dissertations on sociopathy, and in-depth accounts of infamous murderers and their motivations. This, in turn, fuelled my growing passion for such knowledge, driving me to hungrily consume every piece of literature and media related to the subject of murder. Dr. Morris ultimately advised my parents to encourage me to pursue a career in Criminology or perhaps Forensic Science, although, as you may know, I ultimately chose the path of a librarian, allowing me to indulge my insatiable appetite for such content.

Then one day, as my adolescence transitioned into young adulthood, an inconsequential event altered the course of my thoughts. It happened at a roundabout near Tesco in Scunthorpe, a roundabout full of trees. As I navigated the circle, enveloped in the mundane routines of daily life, a chilling notion suddenly seized me: Could one conceal a body within that roundabout, and if so, how would such a macabre act be executed without detection? This unsettling thought, like a seed sown deep within my psyche, took root and began to flourish, its tendrils steadily winding their way through my mind.

From that day on, to the outsider, I might've seemed consumed. I pored over forensic accounts, crime scene photographs, and detailed confessions, each narrative more tantalising than the last. I yearned to understand, to trace the journey from mere thought to gruesome action. How did these individuals plan, execute, and, most intriguingly, evade capture, and could I do it?

As months stretched into years, I constructed elaborate mental blueprints. The act of murder, I realised, wasn't a crude act but a careful ballet that balanced precision with deception. One needed to be methodical, and analytical—a choreographer of chaos.

Humans, with their rich tapestry of behaviours, presented both challenges and opportunities. A casual smile, a fleeting gaze, an innocuous comment—these were tools, weapons even, that could be employed masterfully to construct an airtight alibi, manipulate a potential witness, or even mislead an investigator.

But there's a vast chasm between theory and practice. While I had amply equipped myself with knowledge, I hadn't put it to the test. Here, I found myself on a precipice. To cross over would mean venturing into realms from which there might be no return. Yet the allure was overpowering, like a moth to a light. I found myself wanting to know what it felt like to kill someone, to watch them die right in front of me. I wanted to experience what notorious killers like Ted Bundy, Jeffrey Dahmer, Andrei Chikatilo, and Dennis Nilsen all felt when they killed. The feeling I had just from driving around that roundabout was overwhelming, one that would not go away.

The distinction between contemplation and intention became progressively hazy. I constructed elaborate hypothetical scenarios, each more intricate than the last. Would it manifest as a crime born of raw passion, or would it be a meticulously calculated act? Would I scatter cryptic clues, taunting investigators in a sinister game of cat and mouse? At this point, who knows, but there was an undeniable certainty that I had resolved to take a life. However, the questions that loomed were ones of who, how, when, and the most daunting of all, whether I could summon the courage to follow through with this menacing intent.

In contemplating the commission of such a heinous act, I understood that every decision and action had to be orchestrated with painstaking precision. Each move had to be part of a carefully laid plan, where every conceivable pitfall was anticipated and every possible contingency scrupulously accounted for. The stakes were undeniably high, with no room for error. My singular goal was to execute this dark act without detection, and it was imperative to emphasise that my intention was not to become a serial killer. I sought only to quench a chilling curiosity, to experience the sensation once, and no more.

One day, as I was putting books away at the library, I realised I was stood at this pivotal crossroads, straddling the fine line between morality and madness, the gravity of my decisions bearing down upon me like an oppressive weight. I found myself starting a journey of self-discovery, one that could lead to profound self-realisation or, alternatively, plunge me headlong into the dark abyss of my own creation.

The choice before me was clear—to retreat to the comfort of contemplation or to leap into the uncharted waters of action. But, as I gazed at the rows of books, I understood that the shadows I had been chasing were not external. They were a reflection of my own psyche—a manifestation of the duality of human nature. Was I as evil as all the killers I had studied? Who knows?

Could I reconcile with this realisation, or would I be consumed by the very darkness I sought to understand? The answers lay just beyond the horizon, waiting to be discovered.

I shrugged my shoulders at my thoughts and carried on putting the books back on their dedicated shelves.

The Perfect Plan Unfolds

The idea of crafting an impeccable plan grew stronger with each passing day; a plan so faultless that it would allow me to commit the most heinous act and slip away unnoticed. A plan tailored to perfection that would leave the world baffled. The thrill of the thought was intoxicating, but I was equally aware of its chilling implications.

And so, all the quiet weekends away in my campervan became the backdrop for the birth of this plot. It was here that I started to etch the grand design in my mind, the best plan ever to enable me to fulfill this desire; to feel what it is like to kill. Freeda, my campervan, became my confidant in my plan. I told her my secret, but she never judged me, only helped me.

The initial concern that demanded attention was knowledge itself. How does one even think about orchestrating such a plan? What prerequisites were essential for success? The multitude of intricate details, including the selection of an unsuspecting target, the careful planning of the method, and the subsequent challenges posed by disposing of the evidence, resembled a complex labyrinth that required careful navigation. While the wealth of books I had already consumed had provided some insight, it was evident that I required a deeper well of academic knowledge to fully prepare myself for what lay ahead.

With a newfound resolve, I changed my research to how killers planned their murders—the ones that did, anyway—

going back over all the cases I had read about before. I submerged myself into the abyss of true crime. The public library, my place of work and a place of learning and enlightenment, ironically became the epicentre of my dark education. Books that peeled back layers of the most notorious criminals, documentaries that took a deep dive into the psyche of serial killers, and articles that documented the grisly details of their deeds became my syllabus.

While researching, I stumbled upon an intriguing notion: Women, due to their inherent thorough nature and desire for detail, made far better killers than men because they are quiet killers and don't mutilate their victims. Men tend to kill for sexual reasons, while women kill for reasons like money or revenge. The statement lingered, propelling my resolve further. I wouldn't merely rely on my intuition; the gravity of the task demanded a thorough study.

Every crime, every misstep made by those who'd walked this perilous path before me, was a lesson; I had to learn from everyone's mistakes. I realised this was not a journey of impulse. A swift act wouldn't suffice; I needed the patience of a hunter, the strategy of a chess grandmaster. The plan's gestation could span years, but time, in this case, was a friend, not a foe. I needed the best plan I could assemble, and it needed to be like the best military operation ever.

I didn't limit myself. The digital realm too was scoured for nuggets of information. Stories of those who'd eluded the grasp of the law, of those who'd faded into obscurity after committing the perfect crime, offered lessons in evasion and deception. I had to know how to dispose of evidence and it wasn't just about physical traces; it encompassed a web of alibis, misleading trails, and psychological games.

Over the months, the plan's skeletal structure began to flesh out. From the broad strokes, I started to fill in the very minute details. The method of killing was of paramount importance. Would poison, the silent and stealthy reaper, be my weapon of choice? Or perhaps an artfully staged accident, a misfortune for the victim but a masterpiece of deception for the observer? I had more questions than answers, so I listed all the questions in my head and blended them into the plan, hoping to find answers to them all.

The metamorphosis was unmistakable. Outwardly, I remained the same—an unassuming figure in society's vast tapestry. Yet, in the shadows, I transformed into a mastermind, wearing the cloak of normality during the day, while at night I was the puppeteer of my sinister design. My head was constantly awash with all this information.

The years flowed, and the plan morphed from an abstract idea into a tangible entity. The final piece of the puzzle was set, and my orchestration of the perfect crime stood complete. I had devised the best murder plan ever. The world, blissfully unaware, went about its daily business. But for me, each ticking second was a countdown.

As I stood on the cusp of setting my plan in motion, my emotions were a cauldron of anticipation, anxiety, and an unwavering commitment to my craft. The world was about to witness a crime so seamless that it would forever remain an enigma. I started to feel excited. After all these years thinking about killing someone, I had a foolproof plan to actually go through with it.

For who would suspect that beneath the veneer of the ordinary lurked a mind so calculating? A mind that had plotted for years, waiting for the opportune moment.

The moment had arrived. The plan was set in motion. And the world would never be the same again.

This was the plan ....

THE PLAN

STEP ONE: Research

Even the most meticulous plans are birthed from a seed of curiosity. My journey into this ominous realm commenced, fittingly, with research. I viewed it as a preparatory phase, the foundation upon which my elaborate structure of evil would be constructed. The hunger for information gnawed at me, driving me into a relentless pursuit of knowledge.

The place where I have worked for so many years, the public library, with its vast array of murder mysteries and crime accounts, was my initial destination. My feet echoed off the checkered marble floor, the sound eerily reminiscent of a heartbeat, as I made my way to the true crime section. To the casual observer, I was simply someone who worked at the library, someone who wandered the aisles of books, replacing books the public had returned. They'd see an unassuming woman, lost in the thrall of her job. But they couldn't be more mistaken. I would linger in the aisles of true crime or fiction, reading the books. At least I don't have to check out the books and I could engross myself in them during my lunch. I was very careful, though; I always wear latex gloves when handling books due to the dirt they hold, always have done, which will work in my favour and leave no evidence that I had read these books.

Books with titles like *Killers Among Us* and *Minds of Madness* became my daily companions. I pored over them, not with the ghoulish interest of a common reader, but with the discerning eye of a student. Every modus operandi, every cited motive, and every pitfall into which previous perpetrators had stumbled became notes in my ever-growing journal. Each page was a lesson, a guide to what to do and what pitfalls to avoid. I carried my journal with me everywhere to capture any snippet of useful information that would help me with my plan. It was full of scribbles, sketches, tables of information, websites, quotes, and post-it notes.

The library wasn't just filled with books; the digital age was a treasure trove of information. The internet became my next fortress of learning. I could log in as whomever I wanted, I had a whole tranche of clients' names I could use—sneaky, I know, but bloody brilliant. Forums dedicated to unsolved crimes, articles dissecting the psyche of notorious killers, documentaries, and deep dives into the methodologies of murderers provided insights that books sometimes lacked. The dynamic discussions, the ever-evolving theories, and the intimate, often raw, confessions of killers. I found myself engrossed in the detail, sometimes forgetting where I was.

I remember stumbling across an article dissecting the psyche of Ted Bundy. It was written with a perspective that shifted the focus from the horror of his crimes to the meticulousness of his planning. The audacity with which he operated, the charm he employed as a weapon, and the small details that eventually led to his unravelling. This article was one of many I absorbed, with each adding a layer to my growing understanding. As my passion for my plan grew beyond my control, I couldn't stop reading anything I could get my hands on.

Television, too, played its part. The silver screen's portrayal of crime often walked the line between fact and fiction, but there were gems to be found in the world of documentaries. Programs like *Forensic Files* and *Cold Case Files* showed the scientific side of crime. They delved into the particulars: how a single strand of hair, a forgotten fingerprint, or a slip in one's alibi could turn the tables. Even quotes from murder

TV series went into my journal. My heart pounded every time I captured a snippet of information; it was exhilarating, and I found myself smiling as I wrote them into my journal.

Then there were shows that gave a voice to the killers themselves. Interviews from prison, where these perpetrators, some remorseful and others chillingly indifferent, recounted their deeds. Their voices, sometimes trembling with emotion, other times cold and mechanical, were a window into their souls. I would sit, watching them, hanging on to every word they said, why they killed, how they did it, how they felt, hoping to capture some useful information, learning from every word.

Through these countless hours of study, patterns began to emerge. I recognised that the most successful criminals shared certain traits. They were diligent, and patient, and could detach emotionally when the situation demanded. The realm of murder was not just physical; it was an intellectual game. It required an understanding of human psychology, an ability to predict how people would react, and a capacity to remain three steps ahead of law enforcement. I had to learn all of this.

In the cocoon of my daily routine, my existence was entirely enveloped by this peculiar blend of activities—reading, watching, contemplating, and meticulously recording my thoughts.

Beyond the library's walls, the city continued to bustle along its customary course, with its busy streets, bustling cafés, and individuals absorbed in their ordinary lives, blissfully ignorant of the profound transformation unfolding within the hallowed halls of the city library, where a killer's birth loomed on the horizon.

Slowly, a strange sensation began to emerge from deep within me, gradually spreading like an internal radiance, and I found myself smiling, not just with my lips, but from the very core of my being. I started to feel a fire ignite within me I knew I wouldn't be able to put out now.

My journals transformed into a tapestry of ideas adorned

with a jumble of elements. Newspaper clippings, excerpts from books, snippets gleaned from online articles, and even haunting photographs captured at crime scenes found their place amidst the orderly pages. Colour-coded post-its forged connections among these diverse pieces of information, weaving a complex web of interlinked concepts. To an outsider, it might appear as the fixation of a deranged psyche, but to me, it represented a flourishing blueprint, a roadmap to the unknown that was gradually taking shape.

One evening, following an extensive immersion in a documentary series chronicling the exploits of female killers across history, I reclined and allowed myself a moment of reflection. The ghostly light from the screen bathed my living room in an eerie glow, revealing the multitude of notes that enveloped me. It was then I recognised the immense reservoir of knowledge I had amassed—a composite tapestry woven from the collective wisdom of criminals spanning various eras and backgrounds.

However, knowledge alone proved insufficient; it was the application that held the true key. The transition from theoretical understanding to a practical, actionable plan became the imperative next phase. Armed with the insights gleaned from those who had trodden this dark path before me, I launched into the next chapter of my sinister odyssey.

Yet, it was crucial to understand that this was merely the beginning. While research constituted the initial step of my design, the real labour, the crafting of 'The Plan' still lay ahead. With each passing day, the separation between the diligent researcher and the imminent practitioner of the macabre art of murder blurred a little further. The metamorphosis was in full swing, and there existed no path of retreat.

The next step was to get some real education.

STEP TWO: *Educatio in Extremis*

As I've explained thus far, my research had predominantly relied on books, articles, documentaries, and similar sources. However, to elevate my pursuit to a level of exact perfection, I recognised the necessity of delving deeper into the realm of academic knowledge.

I needed to get inside the head of a killer, to know how they think, to profile them. So, it all began with a simple online search—"Forensic Science Courses Near Me." I soon discovered an accredited institution offering a detailed course on Forensic Science. Additionally, they provided A-level courses in Criminology and Criminal Psychology. It was almost as if the universe conspired in my favour, presenting me with precisely what I sought. I signed up for all three courses and set about absorbing the knowledge they provided.

There's something inherently bizarre about sitting in a sterile, brightly lit classroom, surrounded by fellow students, many of whom were pursuing careers to uphold the law or solve crimes. Here I was, with a motive so deviating, yet outwardly blending seamlessly among them. The irony of the situation loomed profoundly: while they aspired to apprehend individuals of my type, I, on the other hand, sought the very knowledge that could potentially enable my evasion. In a twisted way, it struck me as rather comical, this intricate dance of contradiction and concealment unfolding in the pursuit of my sinister goal.

The first day of the Forensic Science class was uneventful. The room was filled with a mixture of young, eager faces and some older professionals possibly looking to switch careers or enhance their existing skill sets. We were introduced to Professor Lorraine Fisher, an elegant, silver-haired woman with soft, welcoming eyes and a vast wealth of experience in the field of Forensic Science—what she didn't know wasn't worth knowing. Her reputation preceded her; she had been an expert consultant for many high-profile crime investigations, such as the Yorkshire Ripper and Dennis Nilsen, just to name a few, but now lectured on the subject.

Our syllabus delved into a broad spectrum of topics, from fingerprinting to toxicology. But what piqued my interest was the module on trace evidence. This was the cornerstone of many criminal investigations: the tiny, often overlooked fragments left behind at crime scenes, which could be damning for the perpetrator. I needed to learn what to avoid, how to thoroughly clean a room to eliminate any trace of evidence, and any other essential information to incorporate into my plan.

Another week, a particular class on blood evidence held my attention. The room was silent save for Professor Fisher's calm, methodical voice as she described the intricacies of blood spatter analysis. We learned about the angular patterns blood makes when cast from various weapons, how to gauge the force of a blow from the dispersion radius, and, most crucially for me, how murderers can degrade blood samples to render DNA extraction impossible. It was exhilarating and yet again my heart was racing listening to the information, and my passion for this plan grew some more.

Through a series of precisely conducted experiments, we unravelled the profound impact of various chemicals on blood samples. Some proved capable of diluting the sample, while others induced clotting, and a few even disintegrated the very structure of the blood. As I feverishly recorded these revelations, my mind raced with thoughts of their multifaceted applications. With the right concoction, handled with utmost caution, one could effectively destroy any traces of their presence at a crime scene. Perhaps the most intriguing discovery was the creative use of horseradish to camouflage blood, rendering it virtually indistinguishable when subjected to the revealing scrutiny of luminol.

But blood was just the beginning. We dove into the realm of fibres, those insidious little threads that clung to almost everything, without us knowing, and can be the downfall of a murderer. Here, I discovered the materials that were least likely to shed. Synthetic polymers like polyester and nylon, when constructed in certain ways, had minimal shedding. Silk, despite its luxuriousness, was a more natural fibre and, hence, shed profusely. I began to thoroughly note these findings, storing them away for future use, as I would need these to decide what clothes to wear when committing the deed.

Throughout the course, my diligent note-taking resembled a process akin to fitting puzzle pieces together. Each entry in my journal was a crucial fragment, contributing to the ever-evolving picture I was piecing together.

Parallelly, the A-level courses in Criminology and Criminal Psychology offered a deep dive into the human aspect of crime. While the forensic course was clinical and technical, these classes delved into the very psyche of criminals. We dissected case studies, analysed behavioural patterns, and even simulated criminal profiling exercises. It was like I was in a different world when attending these classes, absorbing every little detail passed on to us. I was in my element.

Professor Helena Brant, our Criminal Psychology professor, was a thin, wiry woman with an insatiable curiosity about the human mind. "What drives a person to break the ultimate social taboo?" she would often muse aloud. Through her classes, I began to see that while methods and modi operandi varied, many killers were driven by similar psychological triggers: trauma, the need for control, childhood upbringing or being ridiculed, or simple, inherent darkness.

We also touched upon the criminal's post-crime behaviour: their potential return to the scene, the possibility of them following media coverage, and the ever-present danger of conceitedness leading to their downfall. This knowledge was golden, a guide on what pitfalls to avoid in the aftermath of the act.

One evening, as we sat in a discussion circle, Professor Brant posed a question: "Do you believe some people are born evil, or are they moulded by their circumstances?" A spirited debate ensued. Some argued nature, others nurture. I remained silent, letting the arguments wash over me. In truth, I wasn't sure where I stood on that spectrum. Was my emerging plan a result of innate darkness, an external push, or just my strong curiosity? I pondered on this as I left the class, as the evening sun cast long shadows on the college grounds.

Beyond my scheduled class hours and throughout my workday, I wholeheartedly immersed myself in independent study to excel in my course assignments. The library's crime section, previously my sanctuary, transformed into an extension of my classroom. I scrupulously scoured research papers on cutting-edge forensic advancements, dissected critiques of established criminological theories, and delved into the intricacies of criminal behaviour, probing deeper into the human psyche than I had ever ventured before. Unsurprisingly, the results spoke for themselves, with distinctions gracing all of my assignments. The professor's commendations were particularly encouraging, as she suggested that I consider a career change, given my profound fascination with the subject matter, stating that I possessed the potential to become an outstanding criminologist. Little did she know my plans.

Months flew by in a blur. Each week brought a relentless

cycle of lectures, intricate experiments, and tireless self-study. The weight of my sinister plan, coupled with the demanding rigours of academic pursuit, often left me utterly drained. Yet, an unwavering drive, and an insatiable need to refine my plan, propelled me forward, compelling me to maintain a facade of normalcy despite the mounting pressures.

On the final day of the courses, the professor addressed the class. "Remember," she began, her voice soft yet firm, "the tools and techniques you've learned here are meant to solve crimes, to bring justice. They are a force for good."

I sat there, pen in hand, feeling the weight of her words bearing down upon me. An undeniable sense of guilt began to wash over me as I pondered the enormity of what I was planning. Yet, amidst the turmoil, a flicker of realisation emerged: this force, this knowledge I now possessed, had the potential for both good and evil. It all depended on the hands that wielded it.

As I exited the college for the last time, clutching my course certificates, a curious blend of elation and trepidation coursed through me. I was now armed with the knowledge I had diligently pursued, a scholar in the intricate dance between crime and its unravelling.

With this arsenal of information in hand, I stood on the threshold of the next phase: the daunting task of assimilating, refining, and crafting a meticulously foolproof plan. The classroom had furnished me with the tools; now, it was time to begin the true journey ahead.

STEP THREE: The Geography of Evil

As mentioned before, the idea of killing someone had planted itself in my mind on a blustery day, driving around the roundabout near Tesco in Scunthorpe. Cars flowed around the island, their drivers unaware of the macabre potential of the mini forest at its centre. Could you hide a body in such a daring location? The very audacity might make it the perfect hiding spot, or so I thought.

From that point on, a seed of curiosity grew into an obsession: Every street corner, every desolate alleyway, every abandoned building, every forest or patch of overgrown area, trees by the side of motorways, roundabouts, areas near landfill sites, deep lakes, and vast areas such as the North Yorkshire Moors, Saddleworth Moor, Peak District, the Lake District, and Scotland began taking on a new meaning. Every location I saw began to morph into a potential grave, each seemingly innocent landmark now carrying a sinister significance. They transformed from mere fixtures to potential sites of dark deeds. The very fabric of Great Britain, its undulating landscapes, its pockets of forgotten wilderness, seemed like they whispered secrets of perfect hiding spots to those willing to listen. And with this new lens, my every day became an exploration. From that day on, wherever I went in my campervan,

I started to keep a list of all these places, plotting them on a map.

I've always had a fondness for travelling, which is why I own a campervan. So, my excursions into the outside world appeared ordinary—just a person who enjoys getting away in her camper. Fortunately, my job came with the perk of unlimited holiday days, allowing me to take extended weekends away whenever I pleased.

Nevertheless, whenever someone inquired, I offered explanations like retracing the path of my ancestors or exploring the charming nooks of Great Britain, particularly places I hadn't ventured to before. I would tell people I had a map of the UK with places where I had been and places I hadn't visited before. Little did they know that my real quest was much darker, and the map designated potential dumping sites. I needed to find places that were under everyone's noses and places no one goes. I planned trips away for long weekends and a few weeks away so I could visit more places. And so, the journey began, and the list started to grow.

The Moors up north were the first on my list. A vast expanse of desolate beauty, the land was a mix of peat, heather, and bog, stretching out endlessly. Legends of bog bodies, preserved for millennia in the acidic, anaerobic conditions, came to mind. The bodies of those unfortunate souls became a part of the land, their facial expressions eerily preserved. A body here could remain undiscovered for generations, sinking slowly into the depths of the wet earth. Look at Tollund Man. He was found 2,400 years later! It was also the place where Ian Brady and Myra Hindley buried their unfortunate victims, so it must be a good place to hide a body.

Next, I ventured to the rugged coastlines of Cornwall. The relentless waves, crashing against towering cliffs, echoed the turmoil within me. The many hidden caves carved by the sea over millennia seemed like perfect places. At low tide, one could easily stash something inside, only for it to be concealed once the tide came in. The idea of a body or body parts, hidden in plain sight, just meters away from unsuspecting tourists, carried a perverse thrill.

From the coastline, I turned my gaze inland. The dense forests of the Midlands offered a different kind of sanctuary. Trees stood tall and silent, their roots intertwining deep below, forming a complex, impenetrable web. The forest floor, covered in a thick layer of leaves and decay, could swallow evidence whole, while the sounds of the woodland masked any suspicious activity. But they had to be forests where very few people went. The last thing I needed was a dog digging up my evidence, so I had to be selective with this list.

Old structures, ruins of castles, and abandoned infrastructures dotted the landscape. There was a haunting beauty in these relics of the past. These derelict places, already carrying stories of ages gone by, could also harbour newer, darker tales. Basements of old factories, the hollowed-out remains of ancient strongholds, or the catacombs beneath churches—each held promise.

Amidst my journey, a visit to the Scottish Highlands presented another enticing possibility. The many lochs, deep and dark, held mysteries of their own. Stories of creatures lurking in their depths added to their allure. Could they also hide human secrets, weighted down, to rest in the cold, abyssal plains?

England's vast network of canals wasn't overlooked either. Built during the height of the Industrial Revolution, they crisscrossed the country, often meandering through isolated areas. The murky waters, slow-moving and opaque, could easily conceal something for a long time, especially if weighted down in their vast depths.

Landfill sites, discreetly selected to veil any telltale scents, easily passable by unsuspecting passersby, where the arrival of another unassuming package would scarcely raise an eyebrow, its innocence artfully maintained in plain view. Alongside these, recycling centres stood as mysterious outlets, offering passage for all manner of objects, regardless of their origins, into the hungry jaws of waiting skips, destined for the landfill sites, forever enveloping the secrets they held in a shroud of obscurity.

Lakes and man-made reservoirs found their place on my list of potential hiding spots, their expansive depths harbouring numerous secrets, some even concealing submerged villages.

Throughout my travels, I maintained a journal, discreetly coded, which I kept hidden in my campervan. Each location was marked, not by name, but by a phrase I had devised that would mean nothing to anyone else. Alongside, I noted the ease of access, likelihood of discovery, and any other relevant details, such as CCTV cameras, how busy it was, etc., that would help me decide if it was a suitable dumping ground. These pages in my journal became my dark atlas, a guide to the hidden corners of the nation.

The phrases I created were as follows:

- "The Rebirth Circle": Representing the recycling process, where objects find new life.
- "The Forgotten Vault": A symbol for the landfill, where secrets and discarded items accumulate over time.
- "The Silent Woods": A symbol for remote and secluded forested areas where such grim activities might occur.
- "The Unmarked Graves": Alluding to burial sites or natural burial grounds that lack proper identification or memorials.
- "The Whispering Marsh": Suggesting marshlands or wetlands where secrets may be hidden.

- "The Shrouded Hills": Representing remote and desolate hilly terrains.
- "The Haunted Hollows": Signifying remote valleys or canyons.
- "The Forgotten Path": A symbol for secluded trails and pathways that lead to hidden locations.
- "The Open Fields": The expansive, open landscapes often found in rural regions, where fields, farms, and meadows stretch out as far as the eye can see.
- "The Neighbourhood Square": This symbolises the heart of a residential area, with hiding places in plain sight.
- "Watery Hollows": Large open lakes, natural or man- made.

As my list expanded, intriguing patterns began to surface. Locations near urban centres, though inherently risky, possessed a unique advantage—boldness. After all, who would think to search for a concealed body amidst the bustling heart of a city? Parks, construction sites, and even the labyrinthine sewers of urban landscapes unveiled a myriad of possibilities waiting to be explored.

As the list of potential locations expanded, a creeping apprehension began to shadow my every thought. With each addition, the weight of the impending act grew more palpable, more immediate. It wasn't solely about discovering the ideal spot; it was also about guaranteeing that the act would leave no trace, neither upon the land's surface nor within the depths of my own psyche.

As my planned travel came to a close, I found myself back where it had all begun: that innocent roundabout near Tesco. It appeared deceptively ordinary now, just another unremarkable piece in the sprawling jigsaw puzzle of Britain's geography. Yet, beneath the veneer of the everyday hustle and bustle, the notion of concealing something within its embrace remained tantalising. Amidst the humdrum of daily life, in the heart of the ordinary, the darkest of secrets could lie in wait, patient and ever watchful.

The list stretched long before me, each potential location beckoning with its own unique allure. Yet, in the midst of this search, a profound realisation washed over me—it was not merely about discovering the perfect hiding place; it was an intricate dance with the land's history, its untold tales, and its enigmatic secrets. My mission transcended time, weaving the past, present, and future into a single, unbroken narrative in which I now played an essential role.

In my secret plan, I had sketched out a new world, one where stories weren't spun around heroes or monarchs, but instead revolved around shadows and hushed confidences. Now, the true labour awaited—the art of seamlessly weaving my own narrative into this intricate tapestry, ensuring it remained concealed, yet perpetually lurking beneath the surface.

STEP FOUR: Who to Kill?

Selecting a victim for the unthinkable act was a decision that weighed heavily on my conscience. It had to be someone removed from the inner circle of my life, someone whose absence wouldn't send ripples through the world I inhabited. To get on this gruesome journey, I had to choose a person living on the fringes of society, their existence almost invisible, barely distinguishable from one day to the next. Like many before me, I had a distinct image in mind, carefully crafted through a combination of physical and personal attributes.

In the bustling heart of the city, where countless lives intersected like threads in a vast tapestry of existence, there was one figure who stood out amidst the chaos—John, unnoticed by most, but not by me. For countless days, he could be found perched on the corner near the library, an emotional reminder of life's unpredictability. It was there, amidst the ebb and flow of the city, that our paths crossed.

I approached John one day, feeling a sense of compassion. I decided to get him some food and drink. "Hi, I'm Isla," I introduced myself, offering a cup of tea and a couple of sandwiches. "I've brought you a cuppa tea and some sandwiches. Mind if I sit down for a moment?"

The man, who had grown accustomed to the passing glances of strangers, looked up in surprise. "Isla, is it?" he replied, accepting the offerings. "You're a kind soul. I'm John. Thanks for the tea and food. Yes, sure, please sit down."

"Can I ask why you're living on the streets?" I inquired gently, my concern evident. John's gaze shifted briefly to the ground before returning to meet my eyes.

"No one has ever stopped to ask me that question," he admitted, his voice tinged with surprise and vulnerability.

I quickly reassured him, "You don't have to answer it if you feel uncomfortable. I didn't mean to pry."

After a moment's hesitation, John decided to share a part of his story. "It's okay. I've been living on the streets for many years now, too many to count. I used to have a really good job as a Marketing Director, but the day my wife and daughter were killed in a hit-and-run accident was the day my life stopped," he recounted, a tear rolling down his cheek. "So now, I prefer to live on the streets. It's just easier."

Observing the pain in his eyes, I felt a deep sympathy for his plight. "Would it be okay if I brought you food and drink from time to time?" I asked, hoping to offer some comfort.

John's face brightened with a grateful smile. "Yes, that would be lovely. Thank you for being a kind person." And that was how our connection began, built upon the simple act of reaching out to another human being in need.

A man whose life, once thriving, had crumbled into fragments of despair and homelessness after a fateful hit-and-run incident stole his wife and child away. John's story was one of tragic loss and agonising sorrow, a narrative that had led him to forsake his former life, seeking solace in the harsh embrace of the streets. Beneath his weathered exterior, he remained a kind soul, despite grappling with the relentless grip of depression, a companion born from the void left by his family's absence. His life, though humble and tragic, held within it an essence that had drawn me to him over the years. He was more than a nameless face on the street; he had become a symbol, a paradox of life's frailty and resilience.

Over the years, our exchanges evolved from mere casual conversations to a subtle web of trust woven through acts of kindness—a hot meal here, a warm blanket there—forging an unspoken bond, all part of my plan.

I had always known, deep down, that John would be the one. It was a notion that had danced in the boundary of my thoughts, never quite taking centre stage until now. The realisation settled in, not with a violent jolt but with the gentle grace of an autumn leaf finding its resting place.

Our exchanges are a blend of casual conversation and veiled observation. His eyes, marked by weariness but not defeat, held no suspicion of my true intentions. I had been careful, my gifts a clever ruse to gain his trust.

The plan demanded precision, and John, dear unsuspecting John, fit the design flawlessly. His story was heart-wrenching, a life reduced to seeking refuge on street corners, surviving on the meagre offerings of sympathetic passersby.

The initial step was to approach him with the offer. A warm bed, a hot meal, a respite from the biting cold—he had no reason to decline. Our previous interactions would quell any doubts. And the season was perfect, winter's chill just beginning to claw at the city.

My house, discreetly located in a neighbourhood that valued privacy, was ideal. I had ensured there were no prying cameras or overly nosy neighbours. The dwellings stood aloof, their inhabitants content in their isolated existences, their greetings seldom more than courteous nods.

Every room was to be prepared and sanitised of personal details that could reveal my true nature. I would convert a guest room into John's temporary abode, its decor a carefully constructed façade of normalcy.

This required thought and precision. It had to be clean, efficient, and, most importantly, devoid of pain. John, despite his role in my grand design, deserved that much.

John's disappearance had to be managed. His daily presence at the library's corner was well-known. A gradual distancing, perhaps a faked move to a shelter, needed to be orchestrated.

The more I pondered the details, the more it became apparent that this was not just about fulfilling a dark fantasy or proving a point. It was a form of artistry, a macabre ballet where each step, each twirl, was a carefully choreographed movement leading to a climax that only I could appreciate.

Days turned into weeks as I played out scenarios, fine-tuned details, and gathered the necessary tools. The mundane act of inviting John to my home had been transformed into an intricate plot, each strand woven with care and precision.

During this time, I continued my interactions with John, each conversation laced with an undercurrent of melancholy only I could detect. His laughter, his stories, his simple joys and sorrows—they were like the fading notes of a sad song, beautiful yet tinged with impending doom.

As the chosen day drew near, a strange mix of anticipation and regret began to brew within me. Was it guilt or simply the realisation of the enormity of the act? The answer remained elusive, lost in the labyrinthine corridors of my mind.

Finally, the day arrived. It was time to set the wheels in motion, to step out of the shadows of planning into the stark reality of execution. As I approached the familiar corner where John sat armed with the usual food and drink, a warm smile playing on his lips, my heart skipped a beat.

This was it, the beginning of the end, the first note of a symphony that would resonate only in the hidden chambers of my soul.

"John," I began as I handed the items to him, my voice steady, my eyes betraying no hint of my inner turmoil, "how would you like to spend a night away from this cold? I have a spare room, and I'd be delighted to have you as my guest."

He looked up at me and his eyes widened, a spark of hope igniting within them. He accepted with hopeful eyes, unaware of the sinister threads woven around him. "Thank you, that would mean a lot."

With that, I handed him my address on a piece of paper

along with the date and time, a lifeline to warmth and sustenance. Everything was set, a well-crafted illusion of hospitality that concealed the sinister purpose lurking beneath. Little did he know that his days were numbered. I was going to put him out of his misery.

The overture had been played, and the pieces were set in motion. The players, oblivious to the grand orchestration taking shape, danced to the rhythm of my design. Behind the scenes, orchestrating this dark performance with a mastery known only to me, I stood poised to craft a masterpiece that would forever remain shrouded in the secrecy of my conscience.

STEP FIVE: The Art of Death

As I pushed the hoover around the living room, I found myself wrestling with the idea that deciding to end someone's life is an incredibly heavy burden to bear. It's not a choice to be taken lightly; it's a decision that carries immense moral and ethical weight. The weightiness of this choice is not lost on me, and it lingers heavily in my thoughts.

I'm acutely aware of the profound moral and ethical concerns surrounding such a grave act. It's a decision that goes against my values and the societal norms I've grown up with. The very notion of causing harm and suffering to another human being troubles me deeply.

This ethical dilemma is causing a great deal of inner turmoil within me. I'm constantly grappling with the idea of inflicting pain on someone else and the potential devastation it could bring to the victim's family and friends. The gravity of this decision weighs heavily on my heart and mind, prompting me to reflect deeply on the moral implications of my thoughts and actions.

I was abruptly pulled back to the present when the vacuum cleaner ground to a halt. Once again, it was Apollo's shedding fur clogging the roller. I made my way to the bin to clear it out before returning to the task at hand, allowing my mind to wander once more.

However, there's a peculiar division within me. While I recognise the gravity of this decision and the profound noble concerns it raises, it doesn't trouble me enough to the extent that I, like most people, could never commit such an act. It's as if I'm standing at the edge of a cliff, gazing into the abyss of my own thoughts, torn between the true repulsion of the act and the dark curiosity that continues to beckon me forward. This internal conflict is a source of discomfort, yet it persists, gnawing at the edges of my conscience, driving me to explore the darkest corners of my psyche.

I shook off those moral considerations and refocused on the task at hand: deciding how to proceed. As I opened my laptop, Apollo hopped onto the table and nestled beside me. It was as though he had an innate sense of my activities, always eager to be part of the moment, even if it meant simply lying next to me.

I started searching and it soon became apparent that there are countless methods to kill someone, each more chilling than the last, and I was on a quest to select the most fitting one for John. My determination led me back and forth to my trusted books and the endless web of information. There, I entered an extensive journey through the chronicles of criminal history, scrutinising the stories of infamous killers. I had been compiling a journal that held within its pages a chilling array of methods for extinguishing a life.

As I delved deeper into my research, I uncovered a vast reservoir of sinister possibilities. The journal became a chilling catalogue, featuring gruesome acts such as stabbing and suffocation alongside the more discreet approach of a drug overdose. But my search didn't stop at conventional sources; it extended into the realms of unconventional inspiration. It was during one of my research binges that I stumbled upon the horrific scenes of the television series *Peaky Blinders*. In that grim narrative, I discovered a particularly haunting sequence where a victim was subjected to a nightmarish ordeal. It involved the chilling process of digging a grave, executing the unfortunate soul, setting the remains ablaze, and finally, burying them. It was a stark reminder of how the human imagination could conjure up the most gruesome scenarios.

In the depths of my gruesome research, I unearthed a chilling array of methods to extinguish a life—strangulation, stabbing, the cold precision of a gunshot, the silent despair of drowning, the deceitful ease of poison. Each method whispered its dark allure, beckoning me to choose. I sought not just a means to kill, but the right one—a method that would let me savour the act, yet slip away unseen, untouched by the law. It was a labyrinthine decision, each path fraught with sinister implications, a veritable minefield in the art of death.

I knew that choosing the right method was crucial, not just for John but also for my own sake. It had to be something that would ensure my escape from the clutches of justice, leaving no trace behind. Moreover, the method I selected would determine whether I needed a single dumping location or multiple ones scattered across the city. This decision hinged on the specifics of the chosen method.

After countless hours of contemplation and drowning in research, I reached a conclusion that would seal John's fate. My foremost concern was ensuring that John's passing would be painless, devoid of any struggle. He had endured immense suffering in his life, and I was adamant that his death wouldn't add to that anguish. So, after a thorough process of elimination, I settled on a method that would involve drugging John by administering a substantial dose of sleeping pills, and then proceeding to dismember his body, followed by placing each body part into a bag to make disposal easier.

Why choose dismemberment, I hear you saying? I chose it as the method for my sinister plan because it offers a unique advantage that sets it apart from the typical messiness associated with killers, especially male ones. You see, most killers tend to be hasty and reckless, leaving a gruesome trail of evidence behind. They let their emotions guide their actions, resulting in chaotic crime scenes that practically scream, "I was here!"

My approach will be entirely different. I've spent countless hours studying the particular details of notorious killers and their mistakes. Dismemberment, when done correctly, can be a precise and controlled process. It allows me to disassemble a body methodically, minimising the risk of leaving behind incriminating evidence. I'm not driven by impulsive emotions; instead, I'm coldly calculating, focused on evading capture and leaving no trace. This is what sets me apart and ensures my plan will unfold differently from those reckless killers I've studied. Plus, I am only five-foot-five and I am not strong enough to haul about a grown man's body.

Armed with a morbid purpose, I set off on a chilling task: to ascertain how many parts a human body could be segmented into. Before me lay an anatomical illustration, its human form now a daunting jigsaw. With each division I plotted, the image transformed, morphing into a grisly blueprint for my dark deeds. Methodically, I deconstructed the human anatomy into pieces, crafting a ghastly guide for what was to come.

Seventeen.

Seventeen distinct parts.

The gruesome list unfolded: one head, two upper arms, two forearms, two hands, two thighs, two calves, two feet, one spine, one pelvis, one rib cage, and a singular, morose collection of internal organs.

Each segment was integral to the despicable scheme I was weaving. The precise disposal of each was crucial, a key to keeping my ominous plot shrouded in secrecy. Knowing the number of parts, my mind turned to the next phase: determining the locations for their disposal, each site a silent accomplice to my shadowy endeavour.

In the shadowed corners of my mind, I knew full well that dismembering a human body was no mere task; it was a harrowing journey into the heart of darkness. Even the most notorious of killers, those who had tread this ghastly path before, confessed to the daunting nature of such a horrific deed. This was no simple feat; it was an endeavour that would strain the sinews of my soul, a twisted trial of both physical and mental endurance. In the eerie silence of my thoughts, I often found myself thinking of Dexter, that fictional harbinger of death who found a grotesque satisfaction in his ritual of dismemberment, revelling in the crimson splatter and the grotesque tapestry of severed limbs.

Having made this grim decision, the comparatively straightforward planning phase was now behind me. I turned my focus to readying my body for the gruelling task ahead. My visits to the gym, once routine, had transformed into a relentless pursuit of physical prowess. The clank and grind of weights became my symphony, each repetition a step closer to the monstrous strength I would need. I understood, with chilling clarity, that this newfound physical vigour was not just for show; it was a necessary evolution for the dark, laborious tasks that awaited.

As I pieced together this sinister puzzle, each element of my plan was painstakingly addressed, laying a foundation steeped in dread. Now, it was time to select the final pieces of this morbid mosaic—the disposal sites. These were not just locations; they were the silent guardians of my secret, the final act in a play written in shadows. Each site had to be chosen with care, a crucial cog in the intricate machinery of my ghastly plot. In this game of cat and mouse, where every detail mattered, these hidden graveyards were the key to ensuring that my dark narrative remained untold, whispered only in the hushed tones of the night.

STEP SIX: Surveillance in the Shadows

The concept of concealing seventeen dismembered remains of a once-living being had evolved from a mere abstraction to a tangible reality, a chilling transformation. The death map I had painstakingly crafted wasn't just a collection of lines and annotations; it was a sinister guide to the hidden, to the obscure nooks and shadowed crannies of the world where secrets could fester unseen. Yet, as any master strategist would attest, even the most thoroughly laid plans demand the touch of reality; the cold, hard assessment of the terrain itself. My late father, a seasoned veteran of the Territorial Army, had often spoken of the irreplaceable value of ground reconnaissance. His words echoed in my mind as I contemplated the crucial task ahead: to personally scout each of the seventeen locations I had chosen.

Seventeen clandestine sanctuaries, each a unique haven of darkness and obscurity, emerged from my extensive research. But to weave this tapestry of deception flawlessly, I needed more than just theoretical knowledge. Each site required a rigorous, personal inspection—a scrutiny so detailed that it would leave no stone unturned, no shadow unchecked. Thus began another journey, one not of discovery but of verification.

My weekends underwent a remarkable transformation,

morphing into covert operations where my dependable campervan played the dual role of transportation and command centre. Its unassuming appearance, white with unremarkable decals, allowed me to seamlessly blend into the crowd. These days, no one gave a second glance to a campervan parked in a layby, near a pub, or along a quiet country lane.

Equipped with the essentials of a shadowy vigil—camouflage cream to blend with the natural surroundings, clothes as dark as the deeds I intended to commit, binoculars to observe from a distance, a long-lensed camera to capture the minute details, and an unwavering patience—I set out. After all, in this game of darkness and deception, it's the minute details that often hold the power. The devil, as they say, is in the details, and I intended to acquaint myself with every infernal nuance. Each site, each potential grave, had to be perfect, unnoticeable, and impenetrable to prying eyes. Only then could my sinister narrative unfold in the shadows, a story written in the blood and flesh of my unseen deeds.

In the shadow-laced realms of my grim endeavour, the art of surveillance became not just a necessity, but a craft, honed under the watchful eye of a moon that whispered secrets of darkness. Each potential grave, each hidden corner of the earth I considered for my unspeakable act, demanded a meticulous study.

First, I scrutinised the accessibility of these clandestine locations. How easily could I slip in and out, a ghost in the night, leaving no trace but the silence of my passing? I studied the natural barriers, the fences that whispered of boundaries, and the walls that held secrets. The nearby paths, veiled under the cloak of darkness, became my allies, as did the secluded parking spots, where my vehicle could rest, unseen by prying eyes.

Visibility and exposure—these were the twin demons I grappled with. How visible were these sites from the roads, from the houses with their glowing windows and the streets with their wandering souls? I sought the embrace of nature, the trees and bushes that could shield my actions, and the artificial shadows cast by forgotten structures.

Human traffic was a variable as unpredictable as it was critical. I observed, with a predator's patience, the ebb and flow of people—the rhythms of their daily lives that they unknowingly performed. My visits spanned the spectrum of time, from the sun's summit to the witching hour, noting the presence of residential areas, the potential for witnesses, for eyes that might see too much.

Security measures loomed like spectres over my plans. The unblinking eyes of cameras, the silent alarms lying in wait—these were the traps I needed to evade. I watched for the guardians of these realms, the security patrols, and the watchful neighbours, their vigilance a challenge to my mission.

The environment itself spoke a language of its own. The soil, with its secrets, told me stories of ease or challenge, whispering of the effort needed to breach its surface. Natural formations, water bodies, and cliffs became characters in my narrative, each with a role to play. And the weather, with its capricious moods, became a factor I could neither ignore nor fully predict.

Ownership and legality—these were the chains of the real world, binding the land with rules and restrictions. Who held the keys to these territories? What laws guarded them? I delved into the history of these lands, seeking the weak links in their armour.

But it was the long-term stability that perhaps whispered the loudest warnings. The future was an unknown spectre, looming with threats of discovery through development or the variable whims of nature itself.

In my reconnaissance, I embraced technology and its double-edged sword. The signal strength of my phone, the GPS that could guide or betray—these were the modern tools at my disposal, to be used with caution.

And so, with the thoroughness of a master craftsman, I pieced together the puzzle. The logistical considerations, the proximity to my own lair, the resources within reach—each was a cog in the intricate machinery of my dark design.

Photographs, snapshots of time and place, became my silent advisors, offering views and perspectives that my eyes alone might miss. And through it all, time and schedule were the rhythms to which I danced this macabre dance – the timing of my visits, the planning of my actions, all synchronised to the heartbeat of the night.

In this labyrinth of preparation and foresight, every detail was a thread in the tapestry of my unholy quest—a quest that was as much about the journey as it was about the destination.

And so, in the eerie hush of twilight thoughts, the resting places for the seventeen severed relics of humanity were etched into finality. Each grave, a carefully chosen abode of shadows, was now more than just a mark on a map; they were sanctuaries of silence, cradles for the fragments of a once-whole, now dismembered existence. The final list looked like this:

- Cheviot Hills, Wooler
- Rhinog Park, Dyffryn Ardudwy
- Kielder Water, Hexham
- Barton-upon-Humber/Humber bridge junction roundabout
- Cairngorms National Park
- Hole of Horcum, Pickering
- Priory Water, Melton Mowbray
- Rutland Water, Oakham
- Pentagon Island, Chaddesden, Derby

- The Willows Natural Burial Ground, Barsby, Leicester
- Belmont Tower, Belton, Grantham
- North Lincolnshire Council Household Recycling Centre, Scunthorpe
- Keldy Castle, Keldy
- Old Mine Nature Park, Ashley Park, Uddingston
- Roxby Landfill Site, Scunthorpe
- Saddleworth Moor, Oldham
- Frodingham Grange, Scunthorpe

In the chilling embrace of my campervan, I pondered over these chosen sites, each a silent testament to the grim task ahead. They were not just holes in the ground or forgotten patches of earth; they were the final witnesses to the fragments of life I would soon scatter. Each location, carefully selected for its solitude and secrecy, whispered tales of oblivion, promising to hold the secrets of the seventeen parts in their unyielding embrace.

As I envisioned the act, a cold realisation crept over me. These graves were not merely physical locations; they were the culmination of a journey that had twisted and turned through the darkest corridors of my mind. They represented the endgame of a plan so chilling, so conscientiously orchestrated, that it sent shivers down my spine.

With each site, a piece of the puzzle fell into place, forming a grisly map that only I could decipher. The isolated woodland grove, the derelict industrial site, the forlorn stretch of riverbank—each was chosen not just for its ability to conceal, but for its resonance with the unspeakable act itself. In these desolate places, untouched by the warmth of human life, the remnants would lie, each part a silent monument to the deed.

And as the moon cast its pallid light through my window, I knew that the path I had chosen was irreversible. These graves, these final resting places, were now bound to me, an unspoken pact etched in the very fabric of the night. The seventeen, in their eternal silence, would speak only to the stars, their stories untold, their existence a mere whisper in the vast, uncaring expanse of the universe.

Each surveillance stint was followed by a cooling-off period. I didn't frequent the same place twice in succession and always altered my appearance—different wigs, makeup, and accessories were my allies.

While the meticulous nature of this endeavour could have been draining, for me it was invigorating. Each observation and each minor detail added a layer of realism and tangibility to the plan. The act, though yet to be committed, felt orchestrated in my mind, down to the last exact detail.

The challenge was not just to observe, but to remain invisible, an enigma. But as the days turned to weeks, confidence grew. I wasn't just another face in the crowd; I was the shadow that went unnoticed, the whisper that left no echo.

The act of surveillance transformed me. From a planner, I became an actor, merging seamlessly into the backdrop of every scene, all while taking strict mental notes. The plan was evolving, no longer just a skeletal structure but a living, breathing entity.

As the final location's surveillance concluded, a sense of accomplishment enveloped me. The next phase was set in motion, the culmination of months of planning and reconnaissance. The stage was set; the actors, unknowing, went about their roles. And behind the curtain, orchestrating it all, was me, waiting for the perfect moment to commence the morbid play.

STEP SEVEN: Tools and Equipment

In the chilling, analytical recesses of my mind, I recognised the paramount importance of this stage. In this unsettling domain where the horrific morphed into methodical, the planning phase stood as the hinge upon which the entire operation balanced—poised between success and unravelling. It demanded unwavering attention to detail, a psychic foresight, and an unyielding determination to steer this chilling plan to its gruesome conclusion.

The procurement of tools and equipment for this grim undertaking was a task shrouded in utmost discretion. I was painfully aware of the dangers of leaving a trace, be it through the unblinking eyes of CCTV or the digital footprints of credit and debit card records. With this consciousness, I orchestrated each step of procurement with painstaking precision, ensuring that I maintained the appearance of an ordinary life while cloaking the crucial components of my scheme from prying eyes.

Maintaining an inconspicuous profile was imperative during this preparatory phase. Each acquisition was a calculated manoeuvre, executed with exact care to elude any potential detection. The tools and materials, the accomplices to my grim task, were stealthily stored, shrouded from the gaze of the unsuspecting.

Each item was selected with painstaking care, its purpose scrupulously aligned with the precise methodology I had devised for John's demise and the subsequent disposal of his remains. The list included:

1. Sleeping Pills – The unassuming target of my carefully woven plot would be graced with a mercy beyond his comprehension: a seamless transition from consciousness to oblivion. The method of his ending had been clear from the outset: sleeping tablets, crushed and surreptitiously blended into his food and drink. I procured these tablets with caution, a subtle dance that left no trace. Visiting different pharmacies over time, spacing the purchases to avoid suspicion, always paying in cash. The crushing of the tablets was a ritual, their transformation into a fine powder a testament to the cold, mechanical efficiency that had consumed me. The calculated dose was enough to incapacitate, but not to kill—not at this stage.
2. Plastic Sheeting – The silent witness to the impending horror was acquired in bulk. Its transparency, a harrowing reminder of the act's visibility, was obscured by careful layering. Nights were spent testing various types, touching them, envisioning the vile purpose they were to serve. My bathroom, the chosen stage for this grotesque performance, was fastidiously prepared with a clinical detachment that opposed the horror of what was to come. Its tiles and fixtures, once mundane, now instruments of a sinister ritual. The sheeting was methodically laid out, taped down with chilling precision.
3. Tools for Cutting – In my quest for a precise and powerful cutting tool, I settled on an industrial-strength jigsaw, a significant upgrade from stan-

dard DIY versions. This choice was driven by the jigsaw's robust build and the efficiency of its blade in slicing through challenging materials, such as flesh and bone. To enhance my skills and ensure the tool's effectiveness, I practiced using it on joints of beef and lamb, believing these to closely mimic the intended materials. In order to avoid traceability and unique forensic marks, I gathered a variety of blades from different manufacturers. The jigsaw's design also allowed for straightforward disassembly, which was crucial for its discreet disposal after use. This meticulous preparation and practice with the jigsaw became a concrete expression of my resolute and deliberate mindset. Alongside this, I acquired an assortment of butcher's knives, each carefully chosen for its sharpness. These knives were so keen, so finely honed, that they could glide through skin as easily as a hot blade through butter, initiating the grim process with chilling efficiency. The painstaking preparation of these tools was not just a necessity; it became a ritual, a tangible manifestation of the grim resolve that had taken root within me.

4. Black Bags – Then there were the black bags, mundane yet crucial, chosen to hold each dismembered part. Such trivialities had taken on an almost sacred significance, each choice laden with purpose and meaning. Their quality was of paramount importance. The bags were not merely a method of disposal; they were to be coffins, each one holding a piece of what was once a living, breathing human being. They needed to be thick, resilient, and capable of containing what they were not meant to hold without risk of tearing or leaking. I studied them, testing various brands and types, feeling the material between my fingers, imagining the dreadful cargo

they would soon carry. The size was another vital consideration. They had to be large enough to hold the dismembered parts but not so large as to be cumbersome. Each bag had to be manageable, and capable of being carried without drawing attention. I measured and calculated, turning a decision that most would make without thought into a matter of life and death. The choice of black for the bags was deliberate, a colour that spoke of finality and oblivion. It was a colour that absorbed rather than reflected, a fitting metaphor for the act itself. The bags were the end of a journey, the final step before the body parts were scattered across the dumping sites. The final selection consisted of heavy-duty rubble sacks, designed to endure considerable weight without tearing.

5. Tape – It was the act of wrapping that brought the reality of the plan into sharp focus. The dismembered parts would be wrapped in black bags and then in layers of black duct tape. The tape was chosen with the same care and attention as the other tools, its adhesive strength and flexibility vital to the task at hand. I found myself practicing the wrapping technique on objects around the house, honing the skill until it became second nature. The process was methodical, almost ritualistic. Each wrap of the tape was a step closer to the act, each layer a physical manifestation of the cold detachment that had taken over. The tape served a dual purpose, sealing the contents and adding an extra layer of security. It was also a psychological barrier, a way to distance myself from the horror of what I was about to do. The tape made the parts objects, things rather than remnants of a person. It was a transformation, a dehumanisation that made the act bearable.

In the quiet hours, when the enormity of the act weighed heavily upon me, I grappled with a courage that no amount of planning could bestow—the courage to kill. It was a battle waged within the deepest recesses of my soul, a struggle between the remnants of humanity and a dark fascination that had seized control. The resolve was found in the most unexpected of places: the very mundanity of the planning. The act had become a project, its horror veiled by the cold logic of preparation. Each step, each choice, had distanced me further from the emotional reality of what I was about to do.

I knew I was ready. The planning had been meticulous, and the preparation complete. The pieces were in place, the stage set. The time had come. The days leading up to the act seemed to stretch and warp, each hour an eternity, each minute a torment. The anticipation was a constant companion, a looming shadow, a reminder of what was to come.

I found myself watching John with a detached curiosity, his daily struggles starkly contrasting the complexity of my inner turmoil. He was, in many ways, an innocent in a web that he could not perceive. The plan had become a living entity, its tendrils entwining every aspect of my existence. Friends, family, work—all had become secondary to this dark obsession. I was consumed, driven, and defined by it.

As the day approached, a strange calm enveloped me. Fear, doubt, moral quandaries—all were swept away by the relentless tide of preparation. I was ready, not out of desire but necessity. The choice had been made; the path chosen. The game had reached its final stage, and I was committed to seeing it through, regardless of the cost. In the mirror, I beheld a stranger, a face that had become an enigma, a mind that had breached unfathomable boundaries that should never have been crossed.

The die was cast, the plan in motion, and there was no turning back. It all felt strangely surreal, like a drama in which I was both actor and audience. The intricate, precise plan was the product of a mind both brilliant and disturbed.

The feelings of guilt and trepidation had given way to a chilling detachment. A transformation had occurred, rendering me unrecognisable, capable of executing this dark deed. The realisation that I had crossed a line from where there was no return was both terrifying and liberating.

As I laid out the implements of death, the full gravity of my actions struck me. Yet, there was no turning back. The dark curiosity that had propelled me to this point was now a commanding force, compelling me to see it through.

John's weathered face, marked by life's hardships, haunted me. His smile, his gratitude for the small kindnesses I had shown him, now echoed with irony. But in my twisted logic, I had convinced myself that I was granting him mercy, freeing him from a life of misery.

As the chilling day neared, I found myself rehearsing every step in my mind, every movement choreographed with precision. I visualised luring him into my home, the words and tone that would alleviate his suspicions. I anticipated his dawning realisation as the drugs took hold, too late to alter his fate.

And so, as I stand in the bathroom, amidst the tools of my dreadful intent, the reality of my impending actions descended upon me like a dark shroud. The drugs, the bags, the tape, the knives, the jigsaw—all lay in readiness, each a cog in a machine that had consumed me.

I knew I was prepared. Every detail had been scrutinised; every contingency planned for. The stage was set, and it was time to act.

In the stillness of my mind, I acknowledged there was no turning back. The plan had evolved into its entity, a dark and unstoppable force. The choices had been made; the path chosen. I was ready. The game had reached its final act, and I was resolute in seeing it through, regardless of the consequences. The die was cast, and there was no retreat.

As Apollo and I glanced back at the painstakingly prepared room, I turned away, knowing that my next entry would mark an act that would forever define me.

STEP EIGHT: The Garments of Mystery

The pursuit of murder, akin to exquisitely fine art, necessitates not just detailed preparation but an obsessive, almost passionate attention to the minutest details. For countless years, I've stood as a silent observer of the masses, a sea of individuals so deeply entangled in their pedestrian existences, completely oblivious to the intricate dance of shadows and light that plays out in the hidden corners of the world. My perception, however, was starkly different, honed to a razor's edge. Amidst the apparent chaos of life, I discerned a mesmerising harmony, a haunting beauty in the concept of annihilation. This was far from a mere whimsical desire. It represented a calculated, methodical yearning, a deep-seated obsession to capture and understand the essence of what many consider the ultimate sin. My aim was to grasp the reins of death itself, to explore it not as a passive subject but as its masterful orchestrator.

My perfectly crafted plan was like a complex tapestry, each thread representing a thought, a consideration, woven with deliberate intent and precision. To bring such a design to fruition, the correct attire was of utmost importance. Just as a painter requires a brush to create, and a writer needs a pen to tell stories, a murderer must don an outfit that allows them to dissolve into the shadows, to become a ghost, an untraceable spectre that leaves not even the faintest trace of their existence.

The very idea of committing such an act in one's everyday clothing struck me as ludicrous. Ordinary garments could betray the wearer in mere moments. A single, forgotten fibre, the tiniest residue of one's presence at the scene, and the entire artistry of the deed would crumble into absurdity, the elegance of the act reduced to clumsy, amateurish blundering.

Thus, my research delved deep and wide. I buried myself in forensic science textbooks from my course, absorbing every detail of the methodologies employed in extracting evidence from crime scenes. My studies extended to articles, documentaries, and forensic television shows like *Silent Witness*. I even went as far as to interview retired detectives, cleverly disguising my inquiries under the guise of a novelist conducting research. I thoroughly analysed cases where criminals were ensnared due to their careless choice of attire, learning from their oversights.

The result of this extensive research was a creation that seamlessly blended practicality with an almost poetic sensibility.

After all the research, I opted for a full-body forensic suit, similar to those adorned by professionals dissecting crime scenes. The irony of such a choice was not lost on me. In this attire, I would transform into a harbinger of death, ironically garbed in the uniform of those dedicated to unravelling its mysteries. The suit, fashioned from a highly specialised, non-porous fabric, was designed to leave no trace, to repel any potential fibres that might betray my presence. It served as both a physical barrier between myself and the act and as a potent symbol of my transformation from an ordinary individual to an orchestrator of fate.

To this ensemble, I added a gas mask. Its inclusion lent a surreal, almost otherworldly quality, masking my face in an inscrutable, emotionless guise, effectively erasing any hint of humanity. Though not practically necessary, the mask provided a psychological layer of separation between myself and the deed, transforming me into a being that seemed to transcend mere mortality.

Gloves were, of course, a critical necessity. The hands, those versatile tools of both creation and destruction, required protection, a barrier to isolate them from the physicality of the act. These gloves were carefully taped at the wrists, securing them against any possibility of leaving behind incriminating evidence. My choice of footwear was similarly practical and methodical. I selected wellies for their simplicity and functionality. Their smooth, unembellished surfaces were ideal, leaving no distinctive marks. Like the gloves, they too were diligently taped, ensuring every seam was sealed, every potential point of entry for damning evidence precisely closed off.

Standing before the mirror, clothed in this ensemble designed for death, I confronted the reflection of a stranger. The being that stared back at me was like a figure from a nightmarish vision, a creature born not of emotion or moral quandaries, but of pure, calculated intellect and an unbreakable will. The emotionless gaze of the mask stared back at me, a chilling, almost haunting emblem of the transformation I had undergone.

Dressing in this garb was more than a mere act of preparation; it was a ritualistic transformation. Each piece of the outfit was adorned not merely with care but with a deep, almost sacred reverence. The application of the tape was deliberate and methodical, each strip serving as a physical and symbolic bond between myself and the impending act.

This suit was far more than just clothing. It was a declaration, a physical manifestation of a deeply held philosophy. It spoke volumes of precision, of an unyielding control, and of an understanding that delved far beyond the superficial. It stood as a stark contrast to the disorder and chaos of the world, a testament to a mind that could see through the veil of normalcy, that could embrace the darkness without being tainted by it.

The ensemble was a masterpiece of design and functionality, a work of art in its own right. It was the culmination of months of intense study, of trial and error, a relentless pursuit of an elusive perfection. This suit was the key that unlocked a long-coveted door, one that led to the ultimate understanding, to a power that few dared even to contemplate.

As I moved, the suit became an extension of my being, a second skin that was both a part of me and yet distinct from me. It embodied a paradox, much like the nature of the act itself. It served dual purposes—as a shield protecting me from leaving behind evidence, and as a tool facilitating the execution of my painstakingly planned deed.

Finally ready, the cogs of the plan start to turn. This outfit was the final piece of a puzzle that had begun to form long ago, the last step on a path that I had started with a single, unyielding purpose.

In that defining moment, facing the monster that I had become in the mirror, I experienced an eerie sense of calm, a serenity that transcended mere satisfaction. I had moved beyond the realm of the ordinary and ascended above the trivialities of everyday existence. I had become something else, something more—a being that existed in a realm of its own.

I had transformed into the architect of death, cloaked in the garments of its mysteries, prepared to explore its deepest secrets, to understand its very essence, to become one with its dark, terrifying allure.

The time had come. The stage was set. The ensemble was complete, every piece in place.

I was prepared to kill.

STEP NINE: The Pinnacle of Darkness

As the day faded, its light yielding to the creeping shadows of night, a resonant knock echoed at my door. It heralded the arrival of John, the unwitting character in this ghoulish narrative, unknowingly standing on the precipice of his destiny. The wheels of my carefully laid plan were now in irreversible motion; there was no turning back from this juncture.

This moment, charged with an electrifying intensity, was the one I had been relentlessly preparing for. It represented the culmination of years of painstaking planning and carefully calculated anticipation. As I stood there, on the cusp of the unfathomable, a torrent of emotions surged through me. It was akin to teetering on the edge of an abyss, a voluntary descent into a heart of darkness that I had chosen to embrace.

A question haunted the boundary of my thoughts, an unearthly spectre in the theatre of my mind. How would I feel in the act of taking a life? I had read somewhere, in the depths of my research, that cutting into human flesh bore an unsettling similarity to slicing through chicken, an unnerving parallel that lent a grotesque layer of reality to the imminent act. This notion was simultaneously intriguing and revolting, a stark reminder of the daunting threshold I was about to cross.

John stood shivering on my doorstep, a victim of the

night's chill. I extended an invitation for him to step inside, into the warmth of my carefully prepared abode. "Please, come in. You must be freezing out there," I offered.

"Thank you so much. It's really cold tonight," John replied as he entered.

Inside, I led him into the living room, where we exchanged brief pleasantries. "Would you like something warm to drink, John? Tea or coffee, perhaps?"

"Tea would be great, thank you," he accepted.

After some small talk, I guided him to a guest bedroom. "Here's a room where you can get comfortable for the night. I have some extra blankets if you need them."

"You're too kind. I really appreciate your help," John expressed his gratitude. His eyes, a turbulence of exhaustion and gratitude, flickered with a fleeting connection to mine before he retreated into the seclusion of the room. While he didn't say much, his tired eyes and the hint of a smile conveyed his relief at finding a bed on this cold night.

While John adjusted to the room, I found refuge in the kitchen, immersing myself in the act of preparing dinner. The meal itself was unremarkable, a simple, home-cooked affair, yet instilled with a significance that belied its mundane nature. It was imperative that the veneer of normalcy be maintained. As I cooked, I sneakily crushed a substantial quantity of sleeping pills, procured specifically for this pivotal night. These were to be stealthily integrated into John's food to ensure he succumbed to a profound and undisturbed sleep.

In due course, I beckoned John to the table, announcing that dinner was served. He descended, now clothed in new pyjamas I had thoughtfully provided, his face reflecting an earnest appreciation.

"Please, have a seat," I encouraged, pulling out a chair for him.

"Thank you," he replied, settling into the chair with a sigh of relief.

He devoured his meal with unexpected vigour, yet his silence was a palpable presence, a reverberating echo of his internal monologue.

"This dish is delicious," John finally complimented between bites, attempting to engage in conversation.

"I'm glad you like it," I replied, offering a faint smile.

Throughout our sparse dinner conversation, John's contributions were limited to polite utterances of gratitude. It seemed as though he was ensnared in silent contemplation, pondering the unexpected circumstances that had led him to this juncture.

"Is everything alright, John?" I inquired, noticing his distant gaze.

Eventually, he broke the silence, his voice laden with fatigue. He expressed a need for rest, a subtle cue that the sedatives were beginning to weave their tranquillising spell.

He hesitated for a moment before replying, "I just didn't expect any of this."

"I understand," I said, concealing my intentions with a reassuring tone. "You must be exhausted. I bet you're looking forward to a good night's sleep where it's warm." He just smiled at me.

With that, he headed back to the bedroom, where the drugs would soon take full effect.

After ensuring a respectful interval had passed, I ventured into the bedroom. There, John lay in a profound slumber, a silent testament to the efficacy of the sleeping pills. In my decision to administer such a potent dose, there was a twisted logic at play. The thought of witnessing the extinguishing of life in his eyes was a reality I found myself unable to confront, especially given the tenuous bond that had formed between us. In my distorted rationale, this method seemed somehow more humane, and more merciful. Yet, beneath this veneer of justification, I was acutely aware of the grim truth – I was on the cusp of extinguishing a human life.

A morbid fact lingered in my thoughts – the human body begins its inevitable journey toward decomposition a mere five minutes post-mortem. It's a stark reminder of life's fragility, a poignant contrast between the vibrancy of existence and the inexorable march towards decay. I observed John's prone form, an unwitting subject about to be transformed into a canvas for my grim opus.

Wearing my death outfit and with John enveloped in the clutches of deep sleep, the time had come to enact the final act of my plan. Manoeuvring his body from the bedroom to the bathroom, a mere stone's throw across the landing, proved a mammoth task. His body, bereft of consciousness, was akin to a dead weight.

Before commencing, it was crucial to ascertain that John had departed from the realm of the living. Kneeling beside him, a large kitchen knife gripped firmly in my hand, I positioned the blade over his heart. Counting to three, I marshalled the full force of my body and plunged the knife deep into his chest. The sensation of the blade cleaving through flesh was accompanied by a frenzy of anticipation and dread. I recalled the confessions of serial killers I had studied, their descriptions of the moment of the kill. Dexter's admission, "The first time I killed it made me sick," resonated with a newfound clarity. The tangible reality of taking a life was a burden far heavier than I had anticipated. The noise of the blade's entry was grotesque, and an immediate sensation of nausea overcame me, but I forced it down. I could hear Apollo scratching at the door, eager to join me and see what I was up to, but I chose to ignore him.

As I withdrew the knife, it emitted an eerie sucking sound. Initially, there was no blood, but then it began to flow, cascading like a dam breached. I was momentarily transfixed by the sight, the blood pouring from his chest entrancing me in a gruesome reverie. Shaking off the stupor, I checked for any signs of life. A faint pulse still lingered in his neck. Steeling myself, I plunged the knife in a second time. This time, there was no doubt—John was dead. The act of killing induced an involuntary physical reaction; I barely managed to remove the gas mask before succumbing to the urge to vomit into the toilet. Afterward, I wiped my mouth with the back of my gloved hand and stood, flushing away the evidence of my physical revulsion.

The realisation dawned that the act of dismemberment would inevitably result in unavoidable bloodshed. As I picked up the blade once more, its metallic surface reflecting the dim light with an eerie shimmer, I braced myself for the task ahead. Blood, the very essence of life, now served as a stark testament to its cessation. I prepared myself mentally and physically for the next phase of my plan, my heart pounding with the intensity of a war drum.

The time had arrived for the laborious task I had meticulously prepared for months. I took the kitchen knife in hand and began the methodical process of dismembering the body, joint by joint, cutting through flesh. The most daunting task awaited me—opening up his abdomen. Drawing upon my extensive research, including watching autopsies on television and online, I performed the Y-incision on his torso. Using the jigsaw, I removed his rib cage, the sound of the saw cutting through bone a stark, harsh symphony in the otherwise silent room. One by one, I extracted his organs, placing them in a plastic box. The sensation was unsettlingly squishy, especially the intestines, which slipped through my gloves with an unnerving ease. Completing this task required another hasty retreat to the toilet, my stomach revolting against the visceral reality of my actions.

The next phase involved cutting through the bones. I activated the jigsaw, its mechanical whirr a grim soundtrack to the unfolding horror. I began at the foot, cutting through the ankle bone, the sensation eerily reminiscent of sawing through wood. The jigsaw jerked forward as it completed its pass through the bone. This part, surprisingly, was not as daunting as I had anticipated. One by one, I placed the severed body parts into the bathtub, creating a pile of human remnants.

Taking a moment to catch my breath, I caught my reflection in the mirror, now obscured by plastic sheeting. Staring into my own eyes, I was confronted with the question, "Who the fuck are you?" However, the urgency of the task at hand allowed no time for self-analysis. I shrugged off the observational query and continued with my grim work.

Before long, the bathtub held a total of fourteen dismembered body parts, along with a box filled with organs. The final act involved severing the head from the spin. As I completed this task and held the head by its hair, looking into John's still-peaceful face, a sense of twisted satisfaction momentarily washed over me. He exhibited no signs of pain, a small comfort in the grand scheme of my actions. I pondered over the pieces before me, a fleeting sense of pride in my achievement overshadowed by the dawning realisation of the atrocity I had committed. I had taken a life and dismembered a body. However, there was no time to dwell on these emotions—the plan had to proceed, and time was of the essence.

The next stage involved carefully packaging each body part in black bags and securing them with duct tape. But first, I needed to change my gloves and overalls to ensure a clean grip on the bags, avoiding any additional bloodshed.

I took each black bag, turned it inside out, grabbed a body part and turned it the right way, then proceeded to wrap them with the tape. The process had a surreal, almost festive air to it, akin to wrapping gifts, albeit of a ghastly nature.

Standing back, I surveyed my handiwork, Bernard Gives' confession echoing hauntingly in my mind: "The first time was exhilarating." Now, I could understand the stark contrast he described, the bizarre blend of terror and exhilaration that accompanies such an act. My own experience was a reflection of this discord, a complex concoction of emotions that defied simple categorisation. The task at hand, however, demanded my attention. There was no time to succumb to self-analysis or regret. The plan necessitated swift and efficient action. Each body part, severed limb, and organ had to be dealt with according to my precisely crafted scheme.

The process of wrapping and sealing each part in the black bags was methodical, almost ritualistic. The duct tape served not only as a means of securing the contents but also as a symbolic finality, a sealing of the deed. I had ensured that the new gloves and overalls allowed for precision and cleanliness, leaving no trace of the carnage on the bags.

The black bags, each containing a piece of what was once a human life, were systematically filled and sealed. I approached the task with a clinical detachment, my movements deliberate and precise. The boxes that held these grim packages were ready, their mundane appearance contradicting the contents within.

For the box of organs, I devised a unique solution. Drawing inspiration from agricultural practices, I planned to integrate them into my compost bin. It was a decision born of practicality and a desire for discretion. This method of disposal, while unorthodox, was ingeniously fitting—a return to the earth in the most elemental way.

Having completed the task, I paused to take in the full scope of what I had accomplished. The neatly wrapped packages, the boxes ready for transport, all stood as silent testaments to the grisly work I had undertaken. It was an unsettling tableau, one that underscored the finality of my actions.

Bernard Gives' words continued to haunt me, a chilling backdrop to my own experiences. Yet, in my case, it was a complex tapestry of emotions—fear, exhilaration, and a deep-seated conflict that churned within me. I had traversed a path that few dared to tread, a journey into the darkest recesses of the human psyche.

The act of killing, I realised, goes against the very fabric of our being. It challenges the innate understanding that life is precious and inviolable. And yet, in defiance of this fundamental principle, I had not only taken a life but dismembered it, crossing into a realm of moral transgression from which there was no return.

The turbulent mix of emotions—the rush of power, the perverse sense of accomplishment, the release of pent-up aggression—swirled within me, a turbulence of feelings that defying easy categorisation.

"You feel bad about yourself," said one killer. These words resonated within me, a stark reminder of the moral chasm into which I had willingly descended. The act of killing is fundamentally against human nature, a violation of the unspoken covenant that life is sacred, not ours to take. Yet here I stood, having crossed that forbidden line, grappling with the inner demons that had propelled me to this precipice.

The array of conflicting emotions was like a tempest within me. The adrenaline rush was akin to a fiery torrent coursing through my veins, reminiscent of Ted Bundy's chilling description of holding the power of life and death in his hands. The perverse thrill described by Chikatilo, The Red Ripper of Rostov, Russia, the sense of control, the cathartic release of suppressed rage—all these facets of their experiences resonated with me. It was a chaotic symphony in which I was both the conductor and a captive audience member.

Yet, as the act drew to its conclusion, as I stood surveying the neatly packaged remnants of a once-living being, an overwhelming emptiness enveloped me. This void was profound, unsettling in its depth. It was as though I had become numb to the enormity of my actions, a stranger to myself, lost on a path that had spiralled beyond my control.

With the task completed, I swung the bathroom door open, and Apollo was still sitting there. He gazed up at me, his eyes shifting between me and the bathroom. It was as though he was silently conveying, "We're not so different now, are we? Both of us are killers." In response, he rose and walked away, his tail held high, an air of disdain in his departure.

In this moment of stark realisation, I was confronted with the chilling truth of what I had become. My descent into darkness had brought me face to face with the abyss of my own humanity. Standing amidst the aftermath, I understood that the darkness I had embraced would forever cast a shadow upon my soul, a stain indelible and profound.

STEP TEN: The Sinister Art of Sanitisation

In the shadowed recesses of my mind, a place where reason and morality had dwindled to feeble echoes, a distorted form of artistry had flourished. The mere act of murder had transcended its brutal simplicity, morphing into an elaborate ballet of concealment and deception. This dance demanded more than mere physical prowess; it required an artful finesse, a cunning intellect, and a chilling detachment from the primeval reality of the deeds being committed.

John—poor, unsuspecting John—had departed this world in a manner most peaceful. His passing, though pivotal, had unfolded with an anticlimactic ease, a simple cog in the intricate machinery of my grand design. The real challenge, the true test of my dark craftsmanship, lay in the aftermath: the meticulous erasure of the crime, the handling of the blood, the odours, and the strategic disposal of my tools.

The deed done, my immediate task was to cleanse my abode, erasing any evidence of the night's grim work before starting on my carefully plotted tour of dumping sites. But first, there was the matter of transporting the dismembered remains.

My campervan, an unwitting participant in this grim saga, stood ready outside. Each body part, swathed in packaging crafted with a professional's attention to detail, awaited its final journey. These evil parcels were a testament to my perverse attention to detail, each one painstakingly wrapped and sealed, effectively shielding their ghastly contents from unsuspecting eyes.

The transfer from house to van was conducted in my secluded garden, a space shielded from curious gazes. The procession from my bathroom to the camper was repeated with a practiced casualness, each trip marking a step closer to completion, each body part a piece of a ghastly jigsaw puzzle falling into place. With measured steps and calculated movements, I ferried the remnants of a once-living being to my campervan.

The ensuing journey to the various dumping sites, a plan hatched and refined over months, was no longer a figment of my imagination but a critical phase of my plan. Each location had been selected with the precision of a cartographer; each disposal meticulously calculated to ensure the scattering of evidence.

With the body parts loaded, the focus shifted to cleansing the scene of my dark deed. Standing before the bathroom, now resembling a scene from a horror film, I couldn't help but let out a mirthless laugh at the irony—most of the blood was indeed in the bathtub. The plastic sheeting proved to be a saviour, protecting the walls and floors from incriminating splatters.

This was where my hours of research and preparation came to fruition. The choice of cleaning agents was crucial. Bleach was employed not just to clean but to chemically alter the blood, rendering it untraceable. The application of bleach was a delicate balance—too little would be ineffective, too much suspicious. A thorough steaming followed, ensuring every surface was left pristine, devoid of any visible trace of the night's horrors.

I didn't stop at the visible surfaces; even the underside

of the bath and the U-bend were dismantled and thoroughly cleaned, leaving no nook or cranny unattended.

The wooden floors of the bathroom and landing, natural absorbers of blood, required special attention. Copper sulphate was my chosen agent here, a chemical that would cleanse without betraying its purpose. It was applied with the care and patience of a master artist, leaving the wood untouched and unstained.

Modern detergents, with their active oxygen content, became unlikely allies in my quest. Products like varnish were used to further break down any blood residues, leaving behind only subtle, unrecognisable traces.

The looming challenge of eliminating the scent of death was next. The persistence of the smell of decay could easily undermine all my efforts. Additionally, bowls of vinegar, along with cat litter, activated charcoal, and even coffee grounds, were strategically placed around the house. These everyday items, seemingly innocuous, were transformed into vital tools in my quest for concealment. Their absorbing properties worked tirelessly to mask any lingering traces of the grisly events that had unfolded within these walls. Their pungent aroma masked any underlying odours. The bathroom curtains, potential carriers of the scent, were subjected to a scalding wash cycle, eradicating any lingering evidence.

While the bathroom was devoid of carpets, the rest of the house's carpets received their own treatment. Baking soda, a simple yet remarkably effective solution, was liberally sprinkled over them. This unassuming powder absorbed any residual odours, and after sufficient time, was thoroughly vacuumed away, taking with it the last whispers of death's scent.

As I surveyed the sanitised rooms, a peculiar cocktail of pride and revulsion surged through me. The intricate detail of my plan had paid off. The stage was set, and the path ahead beckoned, leading me towards a future shrouded in uncertainty. Every cleaning material, cloth, and piece of protective wear—anything that had played a role in this night's grim performance—was gathered. These were stowed in a black plastic bag destined for incineration in my firepit, a fittingly fiery end to these silent accomplices.

The thrill of uncertainty, the intoxicating mix of fear and exhilaration, was almost overwhelming as I locked the door behind me and made my way to the campervan. The world, unbeknownst to the horrors that had transpired within my walls, continued its mundane dance. To them, I was just another face, another passerby. But to me, the world had transformed into a grand chessboard, and I had just made a daring, dark gambit in a game that transcended conventional morality and law.

My heart raced, pounding against my chest with the ferocity of a wild drum. The rush of adrenaline, the heady sense of power and control, was unlike anything I had ever experienced. As I settled into the driver's seat of the campervan, the first light of dawn began to creep over the horizon, casting long shadows and heralding the start of a new day.

I gripped the steering wheel, the weight of my secret a heavy, constant presence. As I drove into the early morning, the van's headlights piercing the darkness, a sense of liberation washed over me. A new chapter in my life had commenced, one marked by a descent into an abyss of my own making, guided by the twisted artistry of a mind that had dared to blur the lines between right and wrong.

In my actions, murder had been transformed into a chilling, exhilarating masterpiece, a dark ode to the capabilities of the human psyche when unshackled from the confines of morality and conscience.

As the campervan merged onto the road, blending into the early morning traffic, I couldn't help but feel a sense of triumph, a perverse satisfaction in having executed a plan so intricate, so daring. The road ahead was uncertain, fraught with risks and unknowns, but I was ready. The journey into the heart of darkness had only just begun.

Once the final remnant of my grim deed, the last fragment of human evidence, was discarded, the final cleansing began. It was the campervan's turn to be purged of its dark secrets. Every trace, every speck of evidence had to vanish, as if it had never existed. Incidentally, this ritual of cleansing was a familiar act, a routine I performed with mechanical precision every time I came home from a trip. To the casual observer, the neighbours peeking through their curtains, it was nothing more than a mundane chore. Little did they know, beneath the veneer of normalcy lay a sinister truth, scrubbed away under the guise of routine maintenance.

STEP ELEVEN: A Perfect Alibi: Crafting Innocence

The transition from meticulous planning to the execution of a dark deed left me in a state of profound ambivalence. It was not merely the act itself but the realisation of the depths to which I had sunk. The very essence of who I once was had been altered, and now I was left with a myriad of conflicting emotions that I had never anticipated.

The concept of an alibi had always intrigued me. It wasn't so much about its legal ramifications or even its basic purpose. To me, an alibi was more about psychology, deception, and the art of being somewhere without really being there.

"Do I need an alibi?" I often found myself pondering. If I wanted to commit the perfect crime, the answer was clearly yes. In today's world, with surveillance at every corner and technology tracking our every move, an alibi wasn't just an option; it was a necessity. The thrill of constructing an air-tight alibi was so very exciting.

The first challenge was to find someone who'd vouch for me. Someone believable, trustworthy, and without a hint of doubt in their eyes. This person needed to be beyond reproach. I considered family, but that felt too obvious. Friends were a likely option, but they could be unpredictable. It then struck me—why not use someone with a professional reputation at stake? A doctor, perhaps. I had recently undergone a series of physiotherapy sessions for a minor back issue, and my therapist, Doctor Marlin, had become quite friendly with me. Would he remember if I had an appointment on a specific day and time?

The trickier part, of course, was making sure that while I had an alibi, someone else appeared to be the likely suspect. How does one even begin to commit a crime and frame someone else? It's all about leaving a trail that points to another, all while ensuring you are invisible. If someone else's fingerprints were at the scene, or perhaps a strand of their hair, suspicion would naturally drift their way. It wouldn't be right, but it would be effective.

The art of getting away with any wrongdoing hinges on details. The devil is in them, after all. The most perfect crime isn't about its commission but its aftermath. Anyone can commit a crime, but escaping its consequences requires meticulous planning, foresight, and a touch of audacity.

Therefore, I decided that my alibi's framework was a local charity event. It was no mere social gathering, but a grand affair attended by the town's who's who. It was the very centrepiece of my plan, the foundation upon which my innocence would be constructed.

Weeks before, the invitation had been secured. A prominent member of the committee had come into the library, so I engaged him in casual conversation, full of shared laughter and anticipation for the event. It was a lighthearted exchange, witnessed by others, yet beneath the surface, every word was a carefully laid brick in the fortress of my alibi.

As the event drew closer, I spoke about it openly, sharing my excitement and plans with friends, neighbours, and people I served in the library. I went shopping for a new suit, selecting a sophisticated yet respectable ensemble that would draw eyes and leave an impression. Every action, every gesture was deliberate, yet natural, woven into the very fabric of daily life.

Weeks of careful planning had brought me to this moment. I had constructed my alibi with meticulous precision, leaving no room for doubt, no crack in the foundation. My innocence was a masterpiece, painted with subtle strokes that defied detection. Yet, even as I revelled in the perfection of my craft, I could feel the weight of the impending act bearing down upon me.

The charity gala wouldn't commence until the witching hour of 7:30 PM. By then, John had already graced my abode, devoured his last supper, and lay cold and lifeless on the porcelain tiles of my bathroom, an unspoken invitation to a gruesome task awaiting me.

Yet, I was compelled to cast aside these ghastly thoughts and transform them into the vibrant epicentre of the soirée. I wove through the crowd, a joyful presence, my laughter a resonating echo, my aura palpable. I initiated conversations and clasped hands with insincere warmth, cementing my place amongst the night's illustrious attendees. Amidst this charade, a local photographer captured my visage—a smile etched on my face, a chilling testament to fake innocence, while a sinister secret lay hidden just beyond the revelry.

The night unfolded, and the moment arrived. I slipped away from the charity event, leaving behind a world of elegance and grace and descending into the darkness of my true purpose. My departure was graceful, an accepted interruption in the life of a busy professional. But the real work was only beginning.

I drove to a nearby café, a place filled with truckers and late-night loners. I settled into a corner stall, ordered food, and even chatted with the waitress. All the while, my mind was elsewhere, on a dark deed yet to be done, my presence at the diner merely another calculated step in my plan.

All the time I am acting out my alibi, the act had already been committed. The body lay still, life extinguished, yet my alibi was alive, growing stronger with each passing minute.

Returning to the charity event, I felt a growing sense of detachment, a numbness that permeated my very being. I rejoined the crowd, slipping back into my role, my absence explained and accepted, but I was no longer the same. The laughter rang hollow, the music a distant melody, the faces around me mere masks hiding the true nature of humanity.

The night wore on, and I played my part, dancing with shadows that hid a truth too terrible to comprehend. But as the hours passed, I could feel something growing within me, a sensation that was both foreign and familiar.

It was guilt.

It gnawed at me; a relentless ache that refused to be ignored. I had crossed a line and ventured into a realm where right and wrong were no longer absolutes but shades of grey. I had taken a life, and in doing so, I had lost a part of myself.

In the room where the event was being held, I looked in a mirror, searching for the woman I once was. But all I saw was a stranger, a reflection of a soul altered by a choice that could never be undone.

It was midnight when I finally left, and I made sure I said goodbye to as many people as possible, then headed into the night to catch an Uber home to finish what I had started.

The days that followed were a haze, filled with the mundane tasks of daily life, but beneath the surface, a battle raged. I was torn between the satisfaction of a plan executed to perfection and the torment of a conscience awakened.

I had committed murder, and the world had seen me elsewhere, wrapped in the illusion of innocence. But I knew the truth. I had crafted a lie so perfect that it had become reality, and in doing so, I had lost myself.

The victory was hollow, the triumph tainted by the knowledge of what I had become. I had escaped the judgement of others, but I could not escape myself. The alibi had saved me, but it was also my damnation, a paradox that would haunt me for the rest of my life.

I was left with a haunting question, a query that echoed in the silence of my soul: Was it worth it?

The answer was elusive, hidden behind a veil of uncertainty and doubt. I had succeeded in my dark endeavour, but at a cost I had never anticipated.

I was free, yet I was trapped, caught in a web of my own making, a prisoner of a choice that had forever changed the course of my life.

And as the days turned into weeks, and the weeks into months, I knew that I would never be the same. The act had marked me, and I was left to grapple with the consequences, alone and forever altered.

But my alibi was complete, a living, breathing entity, supported and witnessed by the very people who might later seek to question it. It was an illusion, a mask that hid a truth so terrible that even I shuddered to think of it.

STEP TWELVE: Reflections

Months had slipped away, each one vanishing like a shadow in the night since that pivotal night that irreversibly twisted my very essence. The memories of that night clung to me with an unyielding grip, echoing like ghostly whispers in the recesses of my mind, fixed and haunting. Alone in the dimly lit confines of my bedroom, the enormity of my actions weighed upon me with the oppressive heaviness of a funeral shroud, a relentless reminder of the irreversible path I had chosen.

I often found myself yearning for the simple, mundane encounters with John, our trivial conversations on the way to work. His absence had left a profound void, a silence that seemed to echo his name. Yet, at work, his presence had vanished from memory, as if he were merely a fleeting shadow, now dissipated into nothingness. This erasure from the collective memory of others had made him the perfect victim, a man whose disappearance caused barely a ripple in the fabric of the world.

What had this descent into darkness taught me? This question, like a relentless spectre, haunted the hollows of my psyche, a constant companion in the solitude of my thoughts. In my self-made lair, I carefully dissected every thread of my elaborately woven plan. The layers of forethought, the calculated steps, the chilling precision—they were starkly etched in my mind with unsettling clarity.

As I reflected upon those weeks, I realised the unexpected

lessons that emerged from my grim undertaking. Patience had become a formidable weapon, attention to detail a critical ally, and the art of manipulation second nature. I had unearthed a darkness within, a chilling abyss I never imagined I could embrace. Life at work had resumed its monotonous rhythm, each day mirroring the last. I maintained my façade, performing my tasks with robotic efficiency, all while concealing the quivering shift within—the metamorphosis into a murderer.

The question of whether I enjoyed killing haunted me like an insidious ghost. In the aftermath, a turbulence of emotions engulfed me—a heady mix of power, adrenaline, and an unsettling satisfaction in the flawlessness of my execution. Yet beneath this, a profound emptiness lingered, a stark realisation of a line forever crossed.

The act was a paradox, a dance on the edge of revulsion and attraction. I had become a master of death, deciding another's fate. This role both repulsed and exhilarated me, awakening a primal force within. The shadow that had always lurked at the fringes of my consciousness had now fully enveloped me.

Would I tread this path again? The question lingered, unanswered yet ever-present. The allure of this forbidden journey whispered seductively, growing louder each day. At this crossroads, I was torn between the person I had been and the one I had become. The future loomed like a gathering storm, casting ominous shadows over my thoughts.

Perhaps I might succumb again. The words, once mere contemplation, had become a haunting reality. The barriers that had restrained me crumbled, leaving me on the brink of a dark, uncharted existence. The thirst for control, the hunger for dominance, these forces now pulsed within me.

The adequacy of my plan gnawed at me. It had succeeded, but the aftermath was a harshness of paranoia and self-examination. Every decision, every detail, every move was scrutinised. If I were to kill again, would my strategy evolve? The weeks had taught me the value of adaptation. The world of crime was a dynamic landscape; my initial blueprint was just the beginning. To walk this path again, I would need to evolve, to anticipate new challenges.

Sitting in the faint glow of my room, I recognised I was forever marked by my choices. The weeks that had passed were now permanently stained with the ink of my actions. I learned that the human soul is a fragile vessel, capable of both light and darkness, and that the quest for power leads to moral ambiguity.

As the echoes of that night continued to resound in my mind, I realised there was no escaping the consequences of my actions. The path I had started on was one of no return, leading ever deeper into the shadows. The darkness that had taken root in my soul was now an inextricable part of me, whispering of paths yet to be taken, of deeds yet to be done.

The choices I had made set me on a path both thrilling and terrifying, a journey into the heart of darkness. The future was a tapestry woven with threads of uncertainty and fear, each day a step into the unknown. The darkness within whispered of possibilities, of paths yet to be taken, of deeds yet to be done. As I sat in the dim light, the awareness that I was forever changed by my actions was inescapable, a testament to the transformation within, a metamorphosis into the unknown.

Nights turned into days, and days into weeks, each one punctuated by the relentless ticking of the clock, a constant reminder of the passage of time and the deeds that lay in its wake. The routine of my daily life continued a façade that masked the turmoil that churned beneath the surface. At work, my interactions were mechanical, devoid of any real connection, each conversation a hollow exchange that left me feeling more isolated than ever. I found myself dwelling on the act, replaying it over and over in my mind. Each detail was etched in my memory, a vivid tapestry of sound, sight, and emotion. The planning, the execution, the aftermath—each element a piece of a puzzle that I had painstakingly assembled.

The silence surrounding John's absence was deafening, a void that seemed to grow larger with each passing day. It was as if he had never existed, his memory erased from the minds of those around me. But for me, his memory was a constant presence, a ghost that lingered in the corners of my mind, a reminder of what I had done.

The act of killing had been a revelation, a journey into the darkest recesses of my soul. It had unveiled a part of me that I had never known existed, a part that revelled in the power and control of taking another's life. The act itself was a complex interplay of emotions, a mix of revulsion and exhilaration that left me feeling both empowered and hollow.

The solitude of my bedroom became my sanctuary, a place where I could escape the monotony of my daily life and delve into the depths of my thoughts. In the quiet of the night, I would lie awake, my mind racing with possibilities, with plans for what could be, for what might be. As I sat in the dim light of my room, the realisation that I was forever changed by my actions was inescapable. The choices I had made had set me on a path that was both thrilling and terrifying, a journey into the heart of darkness. The future was a tapestry woven with threads of uncertainty and fear, each day a step into the unknown.

The idea of killing again was both terrifying and intoxicating. It was a path that I knew I could tread, a path that offered a sense of power and control that I had never known before. But it was also a path that was fraught with danger, a path that could lead to my destruction.

As I contemplated the future, I realised that I was at a crossroads, a point of no return. The person I had been was gone, replaced by someone new, someone darker, someone more dangerous. The choice of whether to embrace this new identity or to reject it was one that I would have to make, a choice that would define the rest of my life.

The darkness within me was a siren's call, a call that beckoned me to explore the depths of my psyche, to embrace the power and control that came with taking a life. It was a call that I found increasingly difficult to resist, a call that promised a release from the mundane existence that I had known.

The weeks that had passed had been a journey into the unknown, a journey that had revealed the true nature of my soul. The act of killing had been a catalyst that had awakened a part of me that I had never known existed. It was a part that was both terrifying and exhilarating, a part that was now an integral part of who I was.

The darkness within me whispered of possibilities, of paths yet to be taken, of deeds yet to be done. It was a darkness that promised power and control, a darkness that was both a curse and a blessing. As I contemplated the future, I knew that the path ahead was uncertain, but one thing was clear—I was no longer the person I had been. I was something new, something different, something darker. The transformation was complete, and the journey ahead was one that I would have to navigate alone; a journey into the unknown.

STEP THIRTEEN: Lay Low and Wait

In the wake of the night that had irrevocably altered the course of my life, I found myself submerged in a chilling stillness, the kind that blankets the world in the aftermath of a storm. The deed was done, the performance at the charity event flawlessly executed, but now came the hardest part: the waiting.

The days that followed were like moving through a thick fog, each moment a surreal blend of the mundane and the morbid. I went about my daily routines, the monotonous tasks of my library job, and the casual exchanges with neighbours, all while a gnawing sense of dread coiled like a serpent in the pit of my stomach. My nights were restless, haunted by shadows and the echoes of my deeds.

I kept a cautious eye on the local news, each headline sending a jolt of adrenaline through my veins. But days turned into weeks, and no whisper of suspicion came my way. The body had been disposed of like a military operation, reduced to nothingness in a way that left no trace. Yet the fear of discovery lingered, a relentless ghost hovering just out of sight.

To the outside world, I was the same unassuming librarian, a fixture in the small town, known for her quiet demeanour and love of classic literature. But behind the façade, I was a tumult of emotions, a storm of guilt, fear, and a dark thrill that I couldn't entirely suppress. It was as if I were living two lives: one in the light, the other in a shadowy realm of my own making.

The quiet of the town became oppressive, the silence a constant reminder of the secret I harboured. I found myself wandering the aisles of the library, running my fingers over the spines of books, each title a temporary escape from the reality I had crafted. Yet even among these silent witnesses, I felt their judgement, the weight of their unspoken accusations.

My interactions with others took on a performative quality. Conversations were careful dances, each word measured, each smile a calculated gesture. I was acutely aware of the eyes upon me, the potential for scrutiny in every exchange. The paranoia was suffocating, a thick shroud that I wrapped around myself, invisible to everyone but me.

The town's rhythm continued unchanged, an idyllic portrait of small-town life, but beneath its surface, I sensed a shift. Whispers in the grocery store, sidelong glances at the post office—were they just figments of my overactive imagination, or had the undercurrents of suspicion begun to stir?

I took solace in my nightly routine, the one place where I could drop the mask and confront the reality of what I had become. In the privacy of my home, I would sit in the dim light, a glass of whiskey in hand, staring into the darkness, lost in thought. The walls seemed to close in on me, the silence a relentless echo of my heartbeat.

The waiting became a game, a test of endurance. Each day that passed without consequence was both a relief and a torment, a reminder of the limbo in which I existed. I had committed the ultimate transgression, yet life continued as if nothing had happened.

But the true test came when I heard the news. A body part had been found, not far from town, a gruesome relic of someone's violent end. The details were sparse, but the chill that ran down my spine was unmistakable. But I knew it wasn't part of John as it had not been found at one of my dumping locations.

In the days that followed, the town was abuzz with the news. Speculation ran rampant, theories and rumours swirling like leaves in the wind. I listened, a silent observer, my expression carefully neutral, but inside, a storm raged.

Still, the question that kept whirling around my mind was, had I been careful enough? Had I left any clue, any trace that could lead back to me? The questions tormented me, each one a needle prick to my conscience. The fear of discovery was a constant companion, a shadow that followed me through my days and haunted my nights.

I had to remain vigilant, to maintain the pretence of normalcy while the world around me seemed to teeter on the brink of revelation. The library became my sanctuary, a place of refuge where I could lose myself in the world of words, a world far removed from the grim reality of my actions.

But even in the quiet of the library, the whispers followed me, a ghostly chorus that seemed to grow louder with each passing day. The waiting was torture, a slow unravelling of the threads of my sanity.

And so, I waited, caught in the web of my own making, a spider waiting to see if the vibrations on the strands would signal my downfall. The days turned into weeks, and the weeks into months, and I was left to grapple with the consequences of my actions, alone and forever changed.

But my alibi stood, a living testament, supported and witnessed by those who might one day seek to question it. It was a mask that hid a truth so dark that even I dared not face it. And in the stillness of the night, as I sat alone with my thoughts, I wondered if the waiting would ever end, or if this game of shadows would consume me.

The Haunting Silence

Two years. Two long, excruciating years since I veered off the path of the ordinary, plunging into an abyss of my own making. Two long years since I scattered John's remains across the British Isles. These past two years have been anything but easy. Whenever I step into the bathroom, the memories come flooding back—the grisly images of dismemberment and the blood that seemed to stain every corner. There are moments when I find myself standing in the doorway, unable to tear my eyes away from the haunting recollection of every cut and every saw, while Apollo, my cat, watches me with that knowing look, as if he understands the dark secret that burdens me. I have even thought about moving house because of this.

Over the past two years, I've been living a life of painstaking concealment, methodically erasing any traces of my monstrous act. I've immersed myself in a complicated web of deception, creating a façade of normalcy that hides the darkest corners of my psyche. My days have been consumed by a relentless routine of cleaning, covering my tracks, and ensuring that no one ever suspects the chilling truth that lies beneath the surface. The weight of my actions is a constant presence, a shadow that haunts my every step.

My work in the library carried on as normal, and conversation about where John was only lasted for a couple of weeks before everyone forgot about him.

That night, when I committed an act so sinister, so irreversible, it permanently stained the canvas of my conscience, forever altering the very essence of who I was. It was a murder, not just of flesh and blood, but of the former self that I once knew. Time, in its peculiar, relentless march, had woven a thick shroud of silence over this dark deed. The world, in its vast expanse, remained oblivious and indifferent. There were no blaring headlines to give away my secret; no whispers of my name floated in the wind, tied to the crime. It was as if the universe itself, in some cruel, twisted act of conspiracy, had become an unwitting accomplice to my sin, shrouding my evil in the mundane, at times even allowing the weight of my actions to slip from the forefront of my consciousness.

But today, the tranquillity of an unremarkable day off from work was shattered. The peace of my morning, as I sat immersed in the mundane ritual of breakfast, was violently ruptured. A series of sharp, commanding knocks thundered through the walls of my home, a sudden, jarring intrusion into my secluded world. The sound was alien, a stark, unwelcome anomaly in my life of solitude. Visitors were a rarity in my existence, a life where I, the keeper of a dark secret, would venture out, camouflaged in the anonymity of the crowd, my true nature shrouded in the shadows.

My mind, once a refuge of quiet contemplation, became a tempest of paranoia and fear. Thoughts and scenarios tangled in a frenzied dance of possibilities and dread. Could the embodiment of law and justice be waiting on the other side, ready to drag my sins into the glaring light of day? A cold shiver of terror slid down my spine as I contemplated the ruin of the world I had so painstakingly constructed.

My heart pounded a frantic rhythm, a wild drumbeat echoing the chaos within. Nerves and apprehension clutched at me, the taste of fear sharp and metallic on my tongue, the scent of impending revelation heavy in the air. My legs felt like lead. With each laborious step towards the door, time seemed to stretch into eternity, each movement a herculean effort against the tide of my unravelling sanity. Reaching for the handle, I was gripped by a moment of paralysing indecision. Should I remain cloaked within the shadows of my secret, or confront the unknown that awaited me on the other side of this door?

At this crossroads, torn between an overwhelming desire for knowledge and the primal urge for self-preservation, I found myself wrestling with a decision that teetered on the edge of reason. Yet, driven by an insatiable thirst for understanding, a hunger to know the nature of the intrusion, I steeled myself and turned the knob. My hand trembled as I opened the door to face the unknown, revealing the unexpected figures on my doorstep.

There, standing before me, were the figures I had both dreaded and anticipated—the police. Their eyes, steely and probing, met mine in a silent confrontation, each gaze heavy with unspoken interrogation and suspicion. A fleeting sense of relief, brief and bitter, turned sour as the reality of their presence twisted in my gut like a live wire of dread.

Frozen in place yet gripped by an inexplicable need to know, I watched as their gazes swept over me, their trained eyes searching, probing, seeking. Was this the moment that I had so carefully built could crumble to dust?

"Good evening, madam. I'm Detective Jones, and this is Officer Martinez. We're conducting an investigation into a break-in at your neighbour's. Could we have a few minutes of your time?" he asked, his words mundane yet laden with an undertone of potential doom.

Nodding, my voice barely a whisper, I allowed them entry into my sanctuary, now transformed into a stage for a drama of potential revelation. The threshold of my home, once a secure boundary, now felt like a sheer drop overlooking an abyss of uncertainty and fear.

As they began their line of questioning, the room seemed to constrict around me, the air thick with tension. Every answer I gave felt like a tightrope walk over an abyss, each word threatening to unravel the delicate fabric of my existence. Their presence, once a distant nightmare, was now a tangible, oppressive force in my home, a harbinger of potential doom.

Once both officers were settled on my sofa, Officer Martinez started the questioning. "We're conducting door-to-door inquiries regarding the recent burglary in your neighbourhood. Could I take your name?"

"Yes, it's Isla Wild," I said very quietly. I watched as Detective Jones wrote this in his little notebook. I felt uncomfortable with them knowing my name.

"Thank you. Have you noticed anything unusual or seen anyone acting suspiciously?" he enquired further.

I shook my head. "No, not really. I mean, I haven't seen anything out of the ordinary." Officer Martinez noted down my response.

"That's all right," Officer Martinez said. "We're just trying to gather as much information as possible. Have you heard anything from your neighbours or seen any unfamiliar faces around?"

I paused, thinking. "I haven't noticed anything. Everyone around here usually keeps to themselves."

Detective Jones was polite and understanding. "All right, Isla. We appreciate your cooperation. If you happen to recall or see anything unusual, even minor details, please don't hesitate to contact us." He stood and handed me his business card.

I nodded. "Sure, I will. I hope you catch whoever did it."

Officer Martinez reassured me, saying, "We're doing our best. If you think of anything, no matter how small, it could be helpful."

Once their questions, mundane and routine, were satisfactorily answered, they thanked me for being cooperative and took their leave.

The walls of my once comforting home now felt like the enclosing sides of a trap, closing in around me. The path I had chosen, the secrets I had nurtured in the dark, had led me to this harrowing junction—a crossroads where the spectres of truth and consequence loomed large, inescapable, and all-consuming.

I closed the door behind them, a wave of realisation washing over me in a torrent. I had escaped discovery, yet again, the noose of fate momentarily loosened from around my neck.

In that moment of profound contemplation, the chilling essence of my true nature revealed itself in stark relief. I had crossed a line from which there was no return, stepping into an abyss that forever altered my trajectory. The choice to commit murder had not only rewritten my past but had irrevocably defined my future. The dormant shadows within me had awakened, now pulsating with sinister energy, a dark craving for the adrenaline of the hunt, the thrill of the kill.

Alone with the weight of my deeds, the gravity of my actions pressed down on me with an intensity that was both terrifying and exhilarating. The silence that had once been a shroud now became a mantle of power that I donned with a newfound sense of authority. Leaning against the closed door, an insidious thought slithered into my mind, spreading through my consciousness like a dark, intoxicating poison. A sinister, twisted smile slowly crept across my face as the realisation that I had outsmarted fate, cheated retribution, finally sunk in.

And with that realisation came a dangerous, whispering question in the recesses of my soul, a question that echoed in the silence of my existence, reverberating through the empty corridors of my home. It was a question that, once unthinkable, now held a macabre allure, beckoning me with its siren song.

Should I do it again?

THE END

ABOUT ATMOSPHERE PRESS

Founded in 2015, Atmosphere Press was built on the principles of Honesty, Transparency, Professionalism, Kindness, and Making Your Book Awesome. As an ethical and author-friendly hybrid press, we stay true to that founding mission today.

If you're a reader, enter our giveaway for a free book here:

SCAN TO ENTER
BOOK GIVEAWAY

If you're a writer, submit your manuscript for consideration here:

SCAN TO SUBMIT
MANUSCRIPT

And always feel free to visit Atmosphere Press and our authors online at atmospherepress.com. See you there soon!

ABOUT THE AUTHOR

Outside of her day job, **Dawn Hemmings** loves exploring new places and going on adventures. She's a true wanderer, whether she's travelling around the world or driving through the beautiful roads of the UK in her campervan named Freeda.

Dawn grew up in North Lincolnshire and lives with her two Maine Coons, Banjo and Presley. She has been working in health and safety for more than twenty-seven years. She's achieved academic success with an MSc in Environmental Health and Safety and an MBA. Dawn has also been a hairdresser and a skilled personal assistant.

In her books, she weaves stories inspired by her diverse travels and her fascination with mysteries and murder.

Milton Keynes UK
Ingram Content Group UK Ltd.
UKHW021923260524
442957UK00004BA/25